Sophie Braimbridge   Erica Jankovich RD

Healthy
Eating
for IBS

photography by Tara Fisher

Kyle Cathie Limited

Foreword by the IBS Research Appeal 7

Introduction 8

About IBS 10

How is IBS treated? 14

Managing your diet 16

Symptom-based dietary treatment of IBS 26

What about fluid? 32

The alternative side 34

Shopping and eating out 37

How to use this book 41

Sample menus 42

From the chef 44

Breakfasts and Breads 47

Soups and Salads 57

Starters and Snacks 73

Fish 83

Meat 97

Vegetables and Tofu 107

Pasta, Rice
and Pulses 123

Puddings 133

Index 142

Resources 144

Acknowledgements 144

To Ab who has had to endure many a recipe test. (Sophie Braimbridge)

To my home team Jonty, Tim and Alex for their tireless enthusiasm, encouragement and time. (Erica Jankovich)

Acknowledgements

Sophie Braimbridge:

To Muna and Jenny who have always laughed at my jokes. Thank you.

Erica Jankovich:

To Professor Silk, Wendy and Jane for their continued support.

To John Peters and the IBS Research Appeal for believing in and promoting diet and good nutrition as a valuable part of the management of IBS.

To all my patients past and present who have given me such valuable experience.

To Sophie Braimbridge whom I thoroughly enjoyed working with and who was able to shed some wonderful insight into fibre modified dishes.

To Muna Reyal and Jenny Wheatley from Kyle Cathie for putting all this together so efficiently and producing a lifestyle cookbook that will help IBS sufferers conquer their symptoms and enjoy their food.

Important note

The information and advice contained in this book are intended as a general guide to healthy eating and are not specific to individuals or their particular circumstances. This book is not intended to replace treatment by a qualified practitioner. Neither the authors nor the publishers can be held responsible for claims arising from the inappropriate use of any dietary regime. Do not attempt self-diagnosis or self-treatment for serious or long-term conditions without consulting a medical professional or qualified practitioner.

Published values of the fibre content of foods vary greatly because of different dietary analysis methods. Researchers from the Dunn Clinical Nutrition Centre in Cambridge have developed the most widely used method, known as the Englyst method of analysis. It is their results on which the fibre content of foods and recipes in this book are based.

At any time of the day or night, one in five of us will be suffering from one or more of the many symptoms of Irritable Bowel Syndrome. IBS as it is generally known is not life threatening – but for many, it's a living nightmare with pain, bloating, urgency, diarrhoea, constipation and the embarrassment of wind and soiling being a few of the symptoms that significantly reduce the quality of life of its victims.

From a clinician's point of view, a major headache is that you can't point to a specific spot on a patient's body and say 'There! That's the cause of your IBS.' IBS is a 'functional' disorder… its symptoms simply occur… there are no abnormalities in digestion or in the absorption of fluids and nutrients and no structural abnormalities that can be identified in the gastrointestinal tract. It comes, it goes or it stays – sometimes for years.

Since we launched our research programme through the IBS Research Appeal in 1992 we've identified stress as one of the major triggers of IBS attacks. But there's not a great deal of commonality between IBS cases – episodes can be triggered by a combination of causes, including mental, physical and sexual abuse. They can be hormonal and cyclical… and it's equally true that in many, many instances, IBS attacks are directly related to what we eat and drink.

Because the causes are so varied, modern management strategies favour a multidisciplinary approach to treatment. These include pharmacological treatments directed towards the intestines – often combined with centrally targeted treatments to overcome psychosocial factors that play an important role in triggering attacks: treatments could include physiological explanation of symptoms, psychotherapy, hypnotherapy, cognitive behavioural therapy (CPT) and for stress, the use of mild antidepressants. However, an extremely important component of the multidisciplinary approach to the management of IBS is the different dietary measures that can be applied.

This collaboration between chef Sophie Braimbridge and dietitian Erica Jankovich has produced a clear and authoritative text and wonderful recipes that I am confident will contribute greatly to the dietary management of IBS. In my experience there is no one better qualified to contribute to the field of dietary management of IBS than Erica Jankovich. For a number of years, Erica has carried out a very important role in our IBS research programme and as a member of our clinical team she, more than any anyone else, understands the value of promoting relevant and healthy eating in IBS.

I also feel that this book reflects the goals of the IBS Research Appeal… we seek simply to improve the management of this very common condition. We continue to strive to understand more of the factors responsible for causing the symptoms. We continue to collaborate closely with the pharmaceutical industry in their development of new treatments for IBS and we continue to research and promote dietary measures that can help IBS sufferers. The IBS Research Appeal has always assumed educational responsibilities towards IBS sufferers and during our studies, we have published bulletins, newsletters and books about the condition. These, along with our book *Understanding Your Irritable Bowel,* generate income which allows us to continue our research. Our latest innovation is our website www.please-help-my-ibs.org which we invite you to visit. It offers a question and answer facility that is providing us with more information about the condition while enabling us to address specific questions from sufferers. The IBS Research Appeal is pleased to be associated with this valuable and helpful book.

Professor David Silk MD, FRCP, Director of Research, IBS Research Appeal

For details of the IBS Research Appeal, please send an s.a.e. to IBS Research Appeal, PO Box 18, Crowborough, East Sussex TN6 1ZY.

Introduction

If you suffer from Irritable Bowel Syndrome (IBS), you will be pleased to know that you are not alone. Although it is difficult to talk about, if you did broach the subject with your family, friends and colleagues, you would discover that IBS affects us all at some stage in our life to a lesser or greater degree.

We are not machines; no one's bowels are always regular as clockwork. We all have experienced excessive wind, bloating, abdominal pain, urgency, constipation and diarrhoea at some stage in the past year.

Statistics vary from source to source, but it does seem clear that IBS is more prevalent in the modern world than in developing countries. At any one time IBS has been said to affect up to 25 per cent of people living in the West. We know that of diagnosed sufferers 60–65 per cent are female and 35–40 per cent are male. It is also more prevalent in young adults and is most commonly associated with life-changing and stressful events.

To a large extent IBS is a hidden disease, classified in the medical world as a functional gastrointestinal disorder, meaning that it is not caused by a specific organic disease but rather by a combination of certain symptoms. Many sufferers tend to go undiagnosed for a long time before they take themselves off to a doctor. When they do reach the doctor, it is still difficult for the average GP to put the puzzle together. Some patients have reported that it has taken three visits to different practitioners before the diagnosis was made. There are reports of people who have suffered for five to ten years before seeking help.

The impact of IBS can vary from person to person and from day to day and month to month. Symptoms can range from mildly inconvenient to severely debilitating. IBS can frustrate your emotional, social and professional life. It may result in absences from work and social functions and can also limit your ability to take part in sport and leisure activities.

The good news is that help is available. Although IBS is a recognised and complex condition, we know that it is treatable. Because of this complexity, it is important not to self-diagnose, and although you may think many of your symptoms match those you read about in this and indeed other books, it is important that you visit a properly qualified and experienced doctor.

Your first port of call is your GP, who may refer you to a gastrointestinal specialist. You will receive a full medical run-down, resulting in a clear individual diagnosis. The specialist will then begin treatment, which could involve medication and referral to a specialist dietitian and/or psychologist. Because of its nature and complexity, treatments for IBS can be rather varied. One American survey conducted by the International Foundation for Functional Gastrointestinal Disorders published in 2004 cited the use of 281 different treatments, including drugs, over-the-counter medications, and herbal and dietary supplements. Not nearly as extreme, this section of this book will examine:

► The disease, including symptoms and a susceptibility test for you to complete.
► The respective treatments and a holistic approach to treating IBS.
► General dietary principles and the application of diet to managing and controlling IBS.
► The alternative approaches to treating IBS.

Essentially, this book acts as both a dietary manual and cookbook, guiding you through the different stages of the dietary treatment for your particular type of IBS. Each of the recipes has been specifically developed and scientifically analysed to enable you to build them into your specific IBS diet. However, as explained later on, managing and controlling IBS should be holistic, drawing on a combination of professional medical guidance, lifestyle improvement and specific dietary management.

About IBS

The digestive system

Food and drink move progressively from the mouth down through the oesophagus (gullet) into the stomach, where they are held for a while to allow a certain amount of digestion to take place. They then move into the intestines where they mix with other digestive juices, slowly but consistently passing through the small and then the large bowel. Most nutrient absorption takes place in the small intestine. Nutrients then move from here through the gut wall into the bloodstream where they are transported around the body to be utilised or broken down for excretion. Fluid is slowly reabsorbed in the large bowel, particularly the colon, allowing the stool to form and subsequently be passed. This natural process of the movement of food through the digestive tract is made possible by contraction and relaxation of the muscles lining it, a process known as peristalsis or gut motility.

So what goes wrong in the digestive system of the IBS sufferer? Latest research into IBS seems to indicate that symptoms usually arise from a combination of the following:

▶ Certain microscopic structural abnormalities in the gut lining. It is not yet clear what leads to these abnormalities.
▶ The influence of psychological factors, resulting in heightened sensitivity to pain and changes in normal bowel movement.

Symptoms and signs

Examination by a qualified medical practitioner is important as many symptoms of IBS can mirror those of other bowel diseases. The doctor, if they feel it necessary, will carry out blood tests, an endoscopy (a procedure where a tiny camera is inserted into your digestive tract and the lining of your bowel wall can be examined), x-rays and other tests to rule out other bowel diseases. In the IBS patient no obvious abnormality will be revealed, and this in itself is often a relief for the sufferer. IBS is therefore classified as a functional disorder of the bowel, meaning that it relates to disturbance of the bowel's normal functioning without resulting from any change in the bowel's structure or from any obvious cause. The symptoms of IBS can be physical or neurological in nature.

Physical symptoms

Further explanation of each of the more common physical symptoms is set out below.

Crampy abdominal pain

It is evident that most IBS sufferers experience this symptom. The region of the bowel affected by pain can vary from person to person. When the bowel attempts to move its contents through, the process called peristalsis (described above) is started by contraction of the muscles lining the abdominal wall.

In the IBS sufferer's bowel there seems to be abnormal movement or

Physical symptoms include:
▶ Crampy abdominal pain
▶ Change in bowel habit; constipation, diarrhoea, alternating between the two
▶ Mucus
▶ Wind, flatulence and bloating
▶ Urgency, incontinence
▶ Incomplete bowel movement
▶ Belching
▶ Nausea
▶ Indigestion

Neurological symptoms include:
▶ Anxiety
▶ Depression
▶ Headaches and dizziness
▶ Joint pain
▶ Muscle fatigue
▶ Lack of energy

contraction of the bowel wall as it attempts to move the contents through, and this is what causes the pain. It is also clear from available research that IBS patients have a more sensitive gut with a lower pain threshold than in unaffected people, and this is another reason for their experiencing more marked pain.

Change in bowel habit
Constipation

Constipation means the passage of small, hard and infrequent stools. Some IBS sufferers pass small stools daily, others open their bowels once a week. The condition is often associated with pain and abdominal discomfort, and many sufferers also experience the feeling of incomplete evacuation.

Constipation can occur for a number of reasons. A proper medical examination is necessary to determine whether the problem is purely diet related, or whether it is due to a mechanical obstruction or muscular defect.

Diarrhoea

This means the passage of rapid, loose, watery stools through the colon. In the IBS patient this is likely to be due to an abnormal increase in motility of fluid content (meaning the body is producing more fluid via movement from the tissues into the gut). Diarrhoea is a significant change in normal bowel function, so make sure you can describe your symptoms in detail to your doctor as this can also be an indicator of other gastrointestinal diseases.

Alternating bowel habit

Some IBS sufferers experience what we call alternating bowel habit, meaning that they will go through a period of constipation and then suddenly get a rush of diarrhoea for a few days and then find themselves constipated again.

Mucus

This is produced in the lining of the colon. It acts as a lubricant and a transport medium for the enzymes necessary for digestion. In some IBS patients, due to the increase in contractility, more mucus is produced and can be seen in the stool.

Wind, flatulence and bloating

The gases in our bowel come from what we swallow and the changes that occur to certain foods when they are eaten. Healthy gut bacteria metabolise a type of fibre called soluble fibre (found mainly in fruit and vegetables) to produce energy that can be used by the body and gases. Gases are in most cases hydrogen, carbon dioxide and methane. It has been proved that in certain IBS patients who harbour excessive amounts of sulphur-producing bacteria, extra gases such as hydrogen sulphide and methanethiol are also produced, which result in the passage of foul-smelling flatus (bad smelly wind). The short chain fatty acids act as a fuel source, thus feeding the colonic bacteria to increase their quantity and fermentation rate and therefore to increase production of these bowel gases. So the more bacteria you feed with soluble fibre, the more gases are produced.

The disturbed gut motility patterns that are commonly seen in IBS patients result in poor movement of these gases as well as of solid matter through the bowel. Research has indeed shown that gases tend to move both up and down the bowel, and they have also been seen to accumulate in sections which could give rise to bloating and pain. In some IBS patients, bloating and wind are caused by the inability to move gas properly through the bowel.

Most IBS patients experience bloating and report that it occurs mainly after a meal and progressively worsens as the day moves on. Many also say that it settles after a night's sleep.

Urgency, incontinence

You may also find yourself dashing to the bathroom with little and unsatisfactory results. Urgency is common in IBS and mainly due to a hypersensitivity of the muscles of the rectum. Some people with IBS will also suffer the embarrassment of soiling.

Incomplete bowel movement

This refers to the feeling that when you have opened your bowels you are not yet finished.

Belching

In some IBS patients excessive burping is common. The anxious IBS patient tends to be more susceptible. Usually belching is a natural process and does not indicate that there is a problem with digestion; however it can become excessive and can be worsened by stress. There are some schools of thought that believe it is a learned reaction to the ingestion of food. Measures such as eating slowly, avoiding carbonated drinks, caffeine, and chewing gum are sometimes recommended. Stress reduction and relaxation seem to be of more benefit.

Nausea

The urge to vomit is often experienced by IBS patients. It is said to be due to a slow rate of stomach emptying, particularly in post-infective IBS patients (see page 13), but has also been attributed to enhanced gut sensitivity, which is common in all sufferers.

Indigestion

Dyspepsia or indigestion is brought about by the ultra-sensitive lining of the IBS patient's bowel. Food is ingested as normal, but because of their enhanced gut sensitivity levels, IBS sufferers will experience fullness, sensitivity and indigestion much sooner than non-sufferers.

Neurological symptoms

Some patients experience severely debilitating symptoms not related to their gut. These include problems with an irritable bladder and passing urine, and gynaecological symptoms specifically associated with the female menstrual cycle.

Anxiety and depression

IBS sufferers are often worriers – they have the type of personality which is easily affected by stress. The development of IBS or the worsening of symptoms is often associated with a stressful event or a change in life circumstances.

Research has shown that IBS patients are generally more concerned and obsessed than average about their body functions and the possibility of illness and disease. Disturbances in mood, such as depression and anxiety, can influence the functioning of the bowel. Chemical changes that occur in the brain can affect the gut via a pathway known as the brain-gut axis, resulting in heightened sensitivity to pain and changes in normal bowel movement.

Headaches and dizziness, joint pain, muscle fatigue and lack of energy

These are all well recognised as symptoms of IBS but also of a disease known as fibromyalgia, which is characterised by unexplained aches, pains and fatigue combined with neurological symptoms. A fair percentage of IBS patients may also suffer from this disease.

Fatigue and general malaise are commonly cited by IBS patients, mainly females. It seems that IBS may be related to chronic fatigue syndrome. The cause of these symptoms is not yet fully understood, although subject to much ongoing research.

What are the causes of IBS?

Many people ask how they can go through a good part of their life having absolutely no bowel complaints at all and then suddenly start developing IBS-type symptoms. There is no simple answer to this question and indeed IBS has been seen to develop for a number of reasons. It is a chronic condition, but many of its symptoms are controllable by the correct combination of diet, medication, exercise and lifestyle management.

Poor diet

We all lead busy lives and hardly stop to put any thought into what, where or when we are eating and drinking. The day often passes by without a sensible thought given to food. Our diet is generally low in nutrient balance and low in a suitable mix of fibres. The food we eat is often highly processed or in a reheatable or ready-made form and contains many additives. We certainly don't drink enough water. All of these factors are counterproductive to a normal, healthy, happy bowel habit.

Food intolerance

In certain instances, eating will trigger IBS symptoms. Sufferers immediately start searching for a suspected food allergy or intolerance, but blood antibody and skin-prick allergy testing have repeatedly revealed negative results. It is believed that it is not a specific food that triggers the reaction but rather a hypersensitive gut, overreacting to its contents. These noted intolerances also tend to affect IBS patients one day yet disappear the next. Studies indicate that emotional or psychological stress and tension can make the bowel more sensitive, causing it to be inconsistent in its reaction to certain foods at any given time.

Psychological factors

As mentioned above, the term brain-gut axis refers to the nerve linkages between the gut and the brain. A whole body of evidence exists to support the theory that psychological factors such as anxiety, depression, mood changes and stress affect bowel symptoms and function. Many IBS sufferers will have experienced an episode of abdominal pain and diarrhoea before a stressful event such as an exam or important match. Others will remember becoming constipated when depressed.

Poor motility

IBS patients have developed an abnormal bowel contractility cycle. Researchers believe that this is due to a microscopic structural abnormality in the lining of the gut wall where a specialised chemical involved in gut contractility is released at an abnormal rate, resulting in increased or decreased motility.

Inflammation and increased sensitivity of the gut lining

A hypersensitive gut could arise from a previous gut infection or from a stressful life event in the sufferer's past. Any food that is eaten could cause crampy abdominal pain which arises from an increased sensitivity to distension of the colon or intestines by gases and fluid.

Previous gastrointestinal infection

A previous serious gastrointestinal infection, such as salmonella or shigella, often contracted on a trip to a foreign country, has been shown to correlate closely with patients subsequently developing IBS. This is referred to as post-infective IBS. It seems that such a severe infection results in a long-term

mild inflammation of the gut. The worse the infection, the higher the susceptibility of the person to developing IBS. The anxiety associated with the time of the illness probably further sensitises the gut.

Who is susceptible?

The factors listed below have been seen to be common linkages among those developing IBS.

If you answer YES to the majority of the questions below, you are likely to be susceptible to IBS.

▶ Does anyone in your family suffer from IBS?
▶ Do any of your family suffer from constipation?
▶ Is there any history of psychiatric illness?
▶ Have you had a previous gastrointestinal infection or a serious bout of food poisoning, perhaps while travelling in another country?
▶ Have you had any previous gastrointestinal surgery?
▶ Are you female?
▶ Do you work long hours and at weekends?
▶ Is your job stressful?
▶ Is your private life stressful?
▶ Do you skip meals?
▶ Do you eat at your desk or in front of the TV?
▶ Do you drink more than three cups of caffeinated drinks per day?

If you answer NO to the majority of the questions below, it indicates further susceptibility to IBS.

▶ Do you find time to relax every day?
▶ Do you exercise regularly?
▶ Do you eat at the same time every day?
▶ Do you eat the same amount of food at every meal?
▶ Do you eat a healthy balanced diet?
▶ Does your diet contain fibre?
▶ Do you drink enough water? (See pages 32–33)

Different types of IBS

IBS as a disease has a great variety of symptoms, and treatment is made easier if we classify patients into three predominant types. Over the past 20 years there has been much debate in the medical field as to how to split these patients into different groups, but there seems now to be worldwide consensus that a symptom-based approach to diagnosis is best.

IBS is almost always associated with the crampy abdominal pain normally relieved on defecation. Patients also tend to have the feeling of incomplete bowel movement, they might pass mucus with a stool and also experience abdominal fullness, wind, bloating or swelling. As such, patients are then categorised into those that are:

▶ Constipation predominant
▶ Diarrhoea predominant
▶ Alternating type (between the above two)

Before a specialist can classify you, the above symptoms need to have been noticed for 12 weeks or more (which need not be consecutive) during the past year.

How is IBS Treated?

Holistic treatment

IBS is a chronic, intermittent and relapsing functional disease. Functional gastrointestinal diseases are a group of diseases where there is no specific known identifiable cause but patients have a recognisable set of symptoms. Symptoms can overlap with those of other illnesses, so ensure that you get a proper diagnosis.

In all my experience, I have come to realise that the best approach is a multidisciplinary one. Those IBS sufferers who have examined the whole picture and devoted time to looking into and taking on board all angles of IBS treatment are those who are most successful in managing their symptoms and controlling their IBS.

The four main areas that need to be managed are your:
- Drug regime
- Lifestyle
- Diet
- Fluid intake (see pages 32–33)

It is important for the doctor and dietitian to work together as treatment by pharmacological means must occur in conjunction with dietary management. In many cases the drug treatment prescribed by your doctor will act as an interim measure while the other aspects of treatment are coming up to speed. Drug treatment tends to be either end-organ-targeted (aimed at the gut) or centrally targeted (aimed at the brain).

Lifestyle management involves getting your 'house' in order – having a look at how you run your life or allow your life to be run by others. It involves critically appraising your work versus your social life and leisure time. Importantly this process should also involve taking stock of your exercise and relaxation patterns.

Dietary management is very much centred around the type of IBS you have. It is based on investigating and treating the symptoms you as an individual have. It is often necessary to start by going back to basic guidelines for healthy eating. These are principles we have all learnt before but as a consequence of modern living have let fall by the wayside.

Improving your fluid intake is the easiest aspect of the treatment to understand but the hardest actually to put into practice. The importance of fluid is discussed in more detail later on.

The drugs

It is important to understand that because of the variation in the way IBS affects different people, drug treatments will also affect people in different ways. Some drugs may work for you but not for your friend who also has IBS. For this reason it is important that you establish a good relationship with your treating doctor and are able to talk openly and clearly about how you feel. Also be prepared to do a little chopping and changing with drugs until you find what suits you best.

Many of the drugs used in the treatment of IBS also require that you take them consistently in order to get the desired effect, so you would need to commit to at least two or three weeks before making any decision regarding their effectiveness.

Here is a basic breakdown of the types of drugs you may be prescribed:

End-organ-targeted
- Anti-diarrhoeals – will reduce urgency, make stool output more predictable and improve consistency.
- Anti-spasmodics – will relax the smooth muscles in the gut, improving and moderating contractility, thereby reducing pain.
- Laxatives – soften the stool, making it easier to pass. They can be the bulking type, which are mainly fibre derivatives and work by retaining fluid; or they can be the osmotic type, which soften and lubricate by drawing water into the gut from the body tissues.
- Receptor active treatment – a revolutionary new treatment for IBS, involving a range of drugs that work on certain receptor cells lining the bowel wall by either increasing or decreasing intestinal motility and contractility.

Centrally targeted
Mild anti-depressants are often used in treating IBS, especially when the brain-gut axis is very involved in its cause. Certain anti-depressants are better suited to certain types of IBS, affecting the rate

of movement of contents around the gut. This type of treatment should not be dismissed as an improvement in mood, stress levels and anxiety can have an important effect on bowel function and other IBS symptoms.

It is important to note, however, that drugs by themselves are not the answer. You should follow the dietary management guidelines regardless of your drug regime.

Lifestyle

Your life should take just as important a role in your treatment as does your diet and your drug regime. We all spend too much time on the go and too little time looking after ourselves. IBS is all about you and the way you do things. Have a long hard look at your lifestyle. Take active measures to change the way you live and what you do in a day. Make realistic changes that you can sustain.

Your work

How much time do you spend at work? Are you working realistic hours? Do you allow yourself a break at lunchtime or do you eat at your desk? Are you pressurised at work? On a scale of 1 to 10, how much stress are you under? All this can be changed in order to improve your health. After all, you are far more beneficial to your employer or your business when you are healthy. Think of cutting back, working from home and getting home in time for dinner with your family.

Your exercise

For some people exercise is routine, for others it is sporadic, and for others it is non-existent. We all know that we should be exercising more, so why aren't we doing it? We need to get our priorities right. The benefits of exercise are many, particularly in the management of IBS. Regular appropriate exercise will reduce our stress levels, improve our psychological outlook and aid the movement of stool throughout the digestive system. We need to commit time to activity: it is best achieved if it is part of our daily routine. Recent research claims that a minimum of 20 and a maximum of 60 minutes of moderate exercise a day is more beneficial than two or three visits to the gym in a week. Moderate exercise means a good, fast, purposeful walk which raises the heart rate but doesn't leave you panting. This can easily be achieved by walking to and from work or putting your trainers on and hitting the park at lunchtime or cycling to school.

Stress, relaxation and counselling

Just taking the first steps to investigate your problem, talking to your doctor and allowing him or her to explain the physiological basis to your symptoms will reduce your anxiety level and make you feel better. Your doctor may refer you to a psychologist for counselling, which may involve hypnotherapy, relaxation therapy or cognitive behavioural therapy, all of which have been shown to have beneficial effects in IBS.

Allow yourself time to relax, plan it into a day. Perhaps take up a hobby or enrol yourself into a part-time course. Stop rushing: get up earlier and give yourself time at home and in the bathroom.

Diet

The way in which your diet can be managed to help your IBS depends on your individual symptoms. Research in the field is varied and in some cases inconclusive, but we do know that one diet is not suitable for all IBS sufferers. This book will help to guide you towards individualising your dietary treatment; however, if you are not getting the expected results, please seek further guidance from a properly qualified and preferably specialised dietitian who has had experience in the area.

The available research has investigated three main areas of specific dietary management:

▶ Manipulation of the fibre content
▶ Supplementation of the diet with digestive bran
▶ The identification of food intolerances

Researchers are not yet agreed on the most appropriate dietary management of IBS. However, experience suggests that the best results are achieved with careful attention to the individual's symptoms and by basing the dietary treatment on improving these specific uncomfortable symptoms.

Managing Your Diet

This section of the book starts by showing you how to assess your current diet and explaining the principles of healthy and balanced eating by concentrating on 'getting the basics right'. It then provides insight into the manipulation and management of the fibre content of your diet according to your symptoms.

Assessing your present diet

It is essential that you take an in-depth look at your present diet before coming to any conclusions regarding how to change it to influence your IBS symptoms. Do this by keeping a careful food diary for four to seven days. Record everything that you eat and drink. In addition, record the quantities you consume as well as your associated symptoms each day. The table below represents an example of a food diary and some guidelines as to how to complete it.

The purpose of the food diary is to estimate your dietary intake and/or to determine if you have associated symptoms with certain foods. The accuracy of the result is very much dependent on the completeness of your record, so the more days you can cover, the more accurate the result will be. It is important to:

▶ Try to complete a minimum of four days that are representative of your usual diet.
▶ Record your intake immediately after meals if possible, when it is still fresh in your mind.
▶ Describe all items in detail: for example, 'lean shoulder of beef', not just 'beef'; 'skimmed milk' instead of just 'milk'.

▶ Write down brand names wherever possible.
▶ List quantities in detail, or use common household measures such as slices, scoops, tablespoons and so on.
▶ Indicate your method of cooking: for instance battered cod, boiled rice.
▶ List the ingredients if a dish contains more than one ingredient.
▶ Keep the labels from all pre-prepared meals you eat.
▶ Record how much fat and oil you use when cooking.

Once you have completed the diary you need to make a summary of it and consider whether your eating habits are meeting basic healthy-eating guidelines. Do this by referring to the dietary assessment table opposite to compare your present dietary intake to your recommended intake.

Example of a food diary

DAY	TIME	FOOD ITEM	DESCRIPTION	AMOUNT	FLUID	SYMPTOMS
Monday	8am	Orange juice	Fresh (carton)		200ml (7fl oz)	Indigestion
		Tea	With milk		2 cups	
		Milk	Full-cream	150ml (5fl oz)	In cereal	
		Sugar		2 teaspoons		
		Cereal	Bran flakes	5 tablespoons		
		Toast	Wholemeal bread	1 slice		
		Margarine	Polyunsaturated light	Medium amount spread		
		Jam	Strawberry	1 teaspoon		

Dietary assessment table

QUESTION	ANSWER	RECOMMENDED PER DAY	EXPLANATION	BENEFITS
How many meals a day did you eat?		3 meals	3 meals per day should be enough for most of us. In special medical circumstances you may require smaller meals, but never skip a meal.	Regular meals help increase our metabolic rate, regulate our blood sugar and help our bowels to function at regular intervals.
How many hours were there between each meal?		4–6 hours	Try to eat your meals at evenly spaced intervals of 4–6 hours every day. Do not eat too late or too early.	We are creatures of habit. Regular meals at evenly spaced intervals will help create a regular bowel habit. Eating too early or too late will upset this balance.
How many snacks did you eat?		0–2	It is best from a weight-control perspective if you can get by without snacking. However, if you are going to snack, make it healthy and low in fat.	Calorie intake is better controlled if you can avoid snacking.
How many portions of fruit and vegetables did you eat?		4–5	Eat 5 in total per day. Fruit juice and beans and pulses can count only as one portion each per day.	Vitamin C, carotene, folates, calcium and iron, fibre and some carbohydrate, plus phytochemicals and anti-oxidants (cancer-protective compounds).
How many times a day did you eat carbohydrate (breads, pasta, rice, potatoes and cereals)?		3	Starchy, high-fibre carbohydrate, such as cereals, bread, pasta, rice and potatoes, should make up 50% of each meal.	Carbohydrate for energy, fibre, B vitamins, calcium and iron.
How big were your portions of protein (meat, fish and chicken) at your main meal?		Meat: 75–110g (3–4oz) Fish: 150g (5oz) Chicken: 110g (4oz) Pulses, soy: 150g (5oz)	Stick to smaller portions of low-fat protein on which there is no obvious fat, e.g. skinless chicken or trimmed bacon.	Iron, protein, B vitamins including B12, zinc and magnesium.
How many times did you eat/drink milk, cheese or yogurt?		2–3	Eating low-fat dairy products 2–3 times per day (glass of milk, matchbox of cheese, small yogurt) should ensure a high enough calcium intake.	Calcium, protein, vitamins B12 and B2, vitamins A and D.
Did you eat crisps, chocolate or sweets?		0–1	Obviously, the least you eat of these, the better.	Empty energy, no real nutritional value.
How many teaspoons of margarine, butter or oil did you use?		3–4	Choose lower-fat varieties that are olive oil-based for better heart health.	Essential fatty acids, fat-soluble vitamins D and E.
How many teaspoons of sugar did you use?		0	Be aware of food and drink containing sugar: they contribute to weight gain and tooth decay.	Empty energy!
What did you drink? Water Tea Coffee Alcohol (units)		Water: 2 litres (3½ pints) per day Tea/coffee: 3–4 cups per day Alcohol: 2–3 units for women and 3–4 units for men (on 4–5 days per week)	Keep dehydrating drinks like caffeine-based fluids and alcohol to a minimum. Drink lots of water every day.	Hydration (see page 32).

A balanced diet

Once you have assessed how you are doing, the first step in dietary management for all IBS patients is to get basic eating patterns right. Learn to eat the right nutrients in the right proportions.

All over the world the theory of basic healthy eating is the same. Wherever you come from, the authorities on nutrition are all promoting the 'five food group' theory. The five food groups are:

Carbohydrates

▶ Dietary fibre, calcium and some vitamins such as B vitamins and iron are supplied by this group.

▶ Carbohydrates can be broken down into two basic groups. Simple carbohydrates are more refined and sugary and require minimal digestion to break them down. Complex carbohydrates are unrefined or contain a larger percentage of fibre; these take longer to metabolise.

▶ All carbohydrates are broken down in the bowel to glucose to supply energy.

▶ Breads, rice, cereal, pasta and grains fall within this group.

▶ Eat starchy carbohydrates at every meal.

▶ Have 6–11 portions in total per day. See page 21 for recommended portion sizes.

Fruit and vegetable group

▶ Fruit and vegetables provide vitamins, minerals, carbohydrates and fibre.

Vitamin C is necessary to build the structure of cells and tissues; it aids wound healing and iron absorption; along with carotene and vitamin A it protects against chronic diseases.

▶ Eat this group fresh, dried, tinned, frozen or in the form of juice.

▶ Have 5 servings per day. See page 21 for recommended portion sizes.

Protein group

▶ Protein-rich foods are essential for growth and repair of the body.

▶ Protein also supplies iron, B vitamins, zinc and magnesium, which are all essential for the formation of blood products, the strengthening of the immune system and the healing of wounds.

▶ Animal protein is found in meat, fish and poultry.

▶ Plant protein is found in nuts, seeds, pulses and TVP (textured vegetable protein, such as soya).

▶ Have 2–3 servings per day. See page 21 for recommended portion sizes.

Dairy group

▶ Dairy products provide calcium, protein and vitamin B12 and vitamins A and D.

▶ Calcium is essential, helping to build strong teeth and bones.

▶ This group includes all milk and milk derivatives such as cheeses and yogurt.

▶ Have 2–3 servings per day. See page 21 for recommended portion sizes.

A note on plant proteins

The soya bean is an excellent source of protein, being low in fat and containing no cholesterol. Soya beans have also been shown to have anti-carcinogenic properties. Most importantly for IBS patients, soya and its products contain fibre. TVP (textured vegetable protein) is a soya derivative that has been processed to resemble meat.

Tofu is the curd part of coagulated soya milk sometimes known as beancurd; it can be bought as a solid block or as a soft, cream-like substance, and can be used in stir-fries, salads or casseroles or as a dip or spread.

Tempeh and miso are fermented soya bean pastes, miso having the addition of grains such as barley or rice during fermentation; they can be cooked in a variety of ways.

Fats and sugars

▶ Simple sugars are considered empty energy as they supply only glucose, with no vitamins and minerals. Fats supply energy in the form of fat as well as fat-soluble vitamins which are important for the health of our cell walls and tissues.

▶ Keep the intake of these to a minimum.

▶ To ensure good heart health, concentrate on having mainly monounsaturated fats in your diet, such as olive oil-based products.

Putting it all together on your plate

It is important to start planning a meal by choosing a starchy carbohydrate as its basis. Then consider which fruit and vegetables would go well with it, and finally decide on a small portion of protein-rich food to balance the meal. For any given meal use the plate diagram below to help plan what you are going to eat.

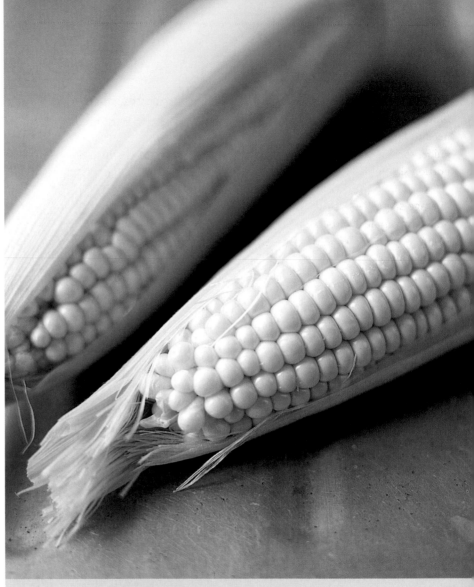

Bread, rice, pasta, cereals, potato etc.

Meat, fish, chicken, pulses, dairy

Fruit and vegetables

Half of your plateful should be in the form of starchy carbohydrate.

One-eighth of your plateful should consist of protein-rich food.

The rest should be made up of fruit and vegetables for the meal (remembering to eat five portions in total per day).

Simple meal plan using the plate method

	STARCHY/COMPLEX CARBOHYDRATE	PROTEIN OR DAIRY	FRUIT AND/OR VEGETABLE
Breakfast	Cereal	Semi-skimmed milk	Banana
Lunch	Wholemeal bread	Tuna	Cucumber and apple
Supper	Jacket potato	Roast chicken, yogurt	Peas, sweetcorn, fruit sal

Portion sizes

Now that you know what to choose, you need to know how much to choose. As a guide, the list below shows the average portion sizes of basic food groups.

Average single serving/portion sizes

Starchy/complex carbohydrates
- 1 slice wholemeal bread
- ½ bread roll
- 4 small crackers
- 1 average bowl cereal
- 1 medium potato
- ½ cup cooked pasta, rice, etc.

Fruit and vegetables
- 1 medium fruit
- 2 small fruit
- ½ cup fruit juice
- 1 heaped tablespoon dried fruit
- ½ cup cooked vegetables
- ½ cup raw leafy vegetables

Protein group
- About 110g (3½oz) or pack of cards-size portion of red meat or chicken
- 2 thin slices ham
- 150g (5oz) fish
- 1 cup cooked pulses
- ½ cup seeds or nuts

Dairy group
- 250ml (9fl oz) mug milk or yogurt
- 30g (1oz) or matchbox-size portion of cheese

Good eating habits

Often just by revisiting the following good, sensible, basic healthy eating practices you will soon start to notice an improvement in your symptoms.

Eating patterns

Try to eat three times a day every day, and if you need to snack, keep the snacks small, regular and healthy. Regular dietary intake speeds up the metabolic rate, which enables you to burn calories more efficiently. The gut has also been seen to respond favourably to regular meal patterns.

Meal timing

Eat your meals at regular and normal times and try and keep these times consistent from day to day. Breakfast is best before 9am, lunch between 12 and 2pm and supper not later than 9pm. Do not skip meals

Food volume

Eat approximately the same amount of food at each meal. Do not have small meals throughout the day and then indulge in a large meal at night. Concentrate on eating the same volume of food from meal to meal.

Eating atmosphere

Eat at a table in a relaxed atmosphere away from distractions and work. Turn the computer and television off and concentrate on what you are doing. Try to create a peaceful, relaxed and calm environment. On working days, consider taking your lunch in the park away from the distractions of an office.

Eating pace

Try to spend 20 minutes eating your meal – don't ever rush it. Think about chewing slowly, and put your knife and fork down between mouthfuls.

The role of fibre

Now that you have established a decent, healthy, balanced diet you will notice an improvement in your symptoms. To consolidate on this further you should next start to investigate the fibre content of your diet. First, a little insight into fibre and its role in the body.

What is fibre?

Fibre is the structural part of a plant, the framework that supports the plant and holds it together. It is therefore a component that is found only in foods of plant origin. It is part of the carbohydrate group, and often referred to as NSP (non-starch polysaccharide) in scientific circles or roughage in layman's terms. It is extremely hardy – you can chew it, swallow it and subject it to stomach acids, yet most of it passes through your body unchanged.

Fibre acts in the bowel to:
- Regularise bowel function.
- Increase faecal weight.
- Improve the time it takes to move the stool through the colon.

There are many types of fibre, but from a dietary perspective we have two major classifications: soluble fibre and insoluble fibre. Plant foods mostly contain a combination of these two types and it is easiest to classify all fibre-containing foods according to which type is predominant. The latest thinking is that bowel function is most benefited by a combination of these two fibre types as they each have a different effect on the gut.

Soluble fibre

Food types which are predominantly high in soluble fibre are:
- Fruits
- Vegetables
- Legumes
- Oats
- Barley
- Seeds

Soluble fibre is effectively broken down by enzyme-producing bacteria present in the colon to produce energy and gas. If you eat too much soluble fibre the stools will be bulky, ribbon-like and hard to pass. Soluble fibre contributes to an increase in bacterial mass of the stool. It forms a gel-like substance which can bind to other substances in the gut, having the additional benefits of lowering blood cholesterol levels and slowing down the entry of glucose into the blood, thereby improving blood sugar control.

Insoluble fibre

Foods predominantly high in insoluble fibre are:
- Roughage foods with skins, husks and peels e.g. spelt, buckwheat, millet, chickpeas
- Some fruit and vegetables with their skins and pips e.g. tomatoes, courgettes, grapes plus potatoes and other root vegetables
- Wheat, rye and all other cereals
- Nuts and some legumes e.g. almonds, chestnuts, coconut, chickpeas
- Rice

Insoluble fibre is less easily broken down by colonic bacteria than soluble fibre but holds water very effectively (up to 15 times its weight in water), thus contributing to an increase in stool weight and making the bowel work more efficiently. It is this fibre that is often referred to as 'nature's broom' and it has been proved to have many protective effects in the gut against diseases like cancer, IBS, Crohn's disease and others.

How much fibre do we need?

There is no simple answer to this question. Each person's fibre intake needs to be individually assessed and the contribution of the different fibre sources in their diet ascertained. This information serves then as a basis for dietary manipulation. It should be noted that there is a very fine line to be drawn between having the correct amount and overdoing it in terms of fibre intake. Prudent guidelines (that is, the recommended average for the population) suggest a total fibre intake of 20–30g per day of which 6–10.5g needs to be soluble. A diet that contains a larger percentage of soluble fibre – that is, greater proportions of fruit, vegetables and pulses to starchy carbohydrates – will perform very sluggishly. The stool will be soft, ribbon-like and hard to pass as it contains no bulk to push against the bowel wall and make the muscle contract naturally. Correct fibre balance will fall into place naturally by following simple healthy eating rules using the plate method (see page 20). As long as you keep the proportions between the food groups right on your plate and stay within your specific fibre allowance, you will achieve a good balance of fibre types. It is important to remember that although these guidelines of 20–30g per day are prudent, they may not be appropriate for you. Your type of IBS and an assessment of your particular symptoms and present fibre intake will determine the amount of fibre that is right for you.

How much fibre do you have in your diet?

Now have another look through your diet these past seven days and, using the fibre table on pages 24–25, assess which group your average fibre intake per day falls into:

Low fibre   0–12g per day
Medium fibre   12–18g per day
High fibre   18–25g per day

How to achieve your optimum fibre intake

There are three different ways of manipulating your fibre intake, which can be summarised as follows.

▶ **By following a healthy natural diet, with careful attention to the types and amount of fibre in foods.**
This option is undoubtedly the best. It will ensure that not only are your fibre sources natural and varied, but also that you can keep a careful control on the amount of fibre you are consuming, bearing in mind that different IBS patients need varying quantities. Your diet will also contain the correct balance of all other nutrients, ensuring a healthy, balanced, prudent intake.

▶ **By eating fibre-enriched foods.**
Foods such as specially produced high-fibre muffins and biscuits or wheat-free, low-starch products will most certainly allow you to manipulate your fibre intake but will not rectify any other dietary imbalances. Such items are often too high in fat and sugar to be considered part of a healthy balanced diet.

▶ **By taking fibre extracts or supplements in the form of bran, pills, tablets, powders and granules.**
Supervised use of bulk-forming laxatives can be beneficial in the early stages of dietary manipulation, but should not be viewed as a long-term solution. Some research has indicated that consistent use of one type of fibre, such as digestive bran, over a long period of time will result in it losing its effectiveness.

Fibre content of basic foods

FIBRE CONTENT OF CEREALS, GRAINS AND BREADS	PORTION SIZE	LOW (0–3g)	MEDIUM (3–5g)	HIGH (6g or more)
Breakfast cereals	**1 average bowl**			
Corn flakes	30g (1¼ oz)	0.3		
Wheat biscuits (e.g. Weetabix)	2 biscuits		4.4	
High-fibre bran cereal (e.g. All-Bran)	40g (1½ oz)			9.8
Muesli (no added sugar)	40g (1½ oz)		3	
Instant hot oat cereal (e.g. Ready Brek)	160g (5½ oz)	2.2		
Puffed wheat (e.g. Sugar Puffs)	20g (¾ oz)	1.2		
Oat porridge (cooked)	160g (5½ oz)	1.3		
Bran flakes	30g (1¼ oz)		3.9	
Fruit and fibre	40g (1½ oz)	2.8		
Sultana bran	40g (1½ oz)		4	
Toasted rice and wheat flakes (e.g. Special K)	30g (1¼ oz)	0.5		
Malted barley extract wholewheat cereal (e.g. Shreddies)	30g (1¼ oz)	2.3		
Whole grain wheat cereal (e.g. Shredded Wheat)	2 biscuits			6.1
Breads and biscuits				
White bread	2 medium slices	1		
Brown bread	2 medium slices	2.8		
Wholemeal bread	2 medium slices		4.5	
Wheatgerm bread	2 medium slices	2.6		
Hi-bran bread	2 medium slices			6.2
Pitta bread (brown)	1 small (75g/3oz)		3	
Granary bread	2 medium slices		3	
Rye bread	2 medium slices	2.6		
Oatcakes	1	0.8		
Digestives	1	0.4		
Rye crackers (e.g. Ryvita)	3 pieces		3.6	
Wholemeal crackers	3 biscuits	1		
Pasta and rice				
White rice	180g (6oz) cooked	0.2		
Brown rice	180g (6oz) cooked	1.4		
White pasta	220g (8oz) cooked	2.6		
Brown pasta	220g (8oz) cooked			8
Pearl barley	150g (5oz) cooked		3	

FIBRE CONTENT OF FRUIT, VEGETABLES AND PULSES	PORTION SIZE	LOW (0–1.5g)	MEDIUM (1.6–3g)	HIGH (3g or more)
Fruit				
Apple (with peel)	1 medium (100g/4oz)		1.8	
Apricots, dried	5 halves			3.4
Apricot, stewed	medium portion (50g/2oz)	1.1		
Banana	1 medium (100g/4oz)	1.1		
Dates, dried	1 (15g/½ oz)	0.6		
Figs, dried	1 (20g/¾ oz)	1.5		
Grapes	small bunch (100g/4oz)	0.7		
Grapefruit	½ medium (80g/3oz)	1		
Nectarine	1 medium (150g/5oz)		1.7	
Melon	¼ slice (183g/6¼ oz)	1.3		
Peaches	1 medium (110g/4oz)	1.4		
Oranges	1 medium (160g/5½ oz)		2.7	
Pears	1 medium (150g/5oz)			3
Plums	1 medium (55g/2oz)	0.9		
Prunes, dried	3		1.7	
Prunes, stewed	6	0.8		

FIBRE CONTENT OF FRUIT, VEGETABLES AND PULSES	PORTION SIZE	LOW (0–1.5g)	MEDIUM (1.6–3g)	HIGH (3g or more)
Raspberries, blackberries	medium portion (60g/2½oz)	1.5		
Redcurrants	medium portion (60g/2½oz)	1.5		
Cranberries	medium portion (75g/3oz)		2.3	
Strawberries	medium portion (100g/4oz)	1.1		
Sultanas	1 tablespoon	0.6		
Raisins	1 tablespoon	0.6		
Blackcurrants	140g (4½oz)			3.9
Gooseberries	140g (4½oz)		2.7	
Rhubarb	140g (4½oz)		1.7	

Vegetables (cooked)

New potatoes	medium portion (175g/6oz)		2.6	
Potatoes, old (no skin)	medium portion (180g/6oz)		1.8	
Potatoes, jacket (with skin)	medium portion (180g/6oz)			4.9
Brussels sprouts	medium portion (90g/3½oz)		2.4	
French beans	medium portion (90g/3½oz)			3.7
Peas	medium portion (70g/3oz)			3.6
Aubergines	medium portion (80g/3oz)	1.8		
Broccoli	medium portion (85g/3½oz)		2	
Carrots	medium portion (80g/3oz)		2	
Spinach	medium portion (90g/3½oz)		1.9	
Tomatoes	medium portion (85g/3½oz)	0.9		
Sweetcorn	medium portion (85g/3½oz)	1.2		
Cabbage	medium portion (95g/3¾oz)		1.7	
Courgettes	medium portion (100g/4oz)	1.2		
Leeks	medium portion (75g/3oz)	1.3		
Parsnips	medium portion (65g/2½oz)			3

Salad/vegetables (raw)

Beansprouts	1 tablespoon	0.3		
Beetroot	1 portion (100g/4oz)		1.9	
Cabbage	medium portion (90g/3½oz)		2.2	
Celery	1 stick (30g/1¼oz)	0.4		
Cucumber	1 slice (6g/¼oz)	0.1		
Lettuce	1 portion (20g/¾oz)	0.2		
Mushrooms	1 medium (10g/½oz)	0.1		
Onions	1 medium (60g/2½oz)	0.8		
Spring onions	1 bulb (10g/½oz)	0.2		
Peppers	1 slice (10g/½oz)	0.2		
Radishes	1 medium (8g/½oz)	0.1		
Tomatoes	1 medium (85g/3½oz)	0.9		

Legumes/pulses/nuts

Aduki, kidney, haricot, black eye beans (boiled)	medium portion (60g/2½oz)			3.3
Split peas, lentils (boiled)	medium portion (60g/2½oz)		1.6	
Baked beans	medium portion (135g/4½oz)			4.7
Borlotti, cannellini, butter beans	medium portion (60g/2½oz)		2.8	
Chickpeas (boiled)	medium portion (60g/2½oz)		2.6	
Almonds	25g (1oz)	1.9		
Coconut	25g (1oz)	1.8		
Hazelnuts	25g (1oz)	1.6		
Peanuts	25g (1oz)	1.6		
Brazil	25g (1oz)	1.1		
Walnuts	25g (1oz)	0.9		

Symptom-based Dietary Treatment of IBS

With a better understanding of how to eat a healthy balanced diet and of the science behind fibre, we can focus on your symptoms and show you how to manipulate your diet according to your bowel function by using fibre.

Most types of IBS will always be associated with crampy abdominal pain, sometimes relieved on defecation. Most patients will also experience abdominal fullness, wind, bloating and swelling. Therefore we assess which group you fall into on a basis of your bowel movements. Are they:

► Constipation predominant?
► Diarrhoea predominant?
► Alternating between constipation and diarrhoea?

Use the recommendations for your type of IBS as set out below to work out how to manipulate your fibre intake. The recipes in this book are classified as being either low, medium or high fibre so that you can choose appropriate meals for your specific needs. See page 41 for more information on using the recipes.

The constipation predominant sufferer

If this is you, you need more fibre in your diet. Having assessed your fibre intake, you now need to start increasing it gradually from low to high. Too rapid an increase will result in pain, cramping and possibly even diarrhoea, which will result in you losing confidence in the treatment and not carrying it through. Take it slowly and aim to increase your intake by just 5g fibre per day over a period of three to four weeks.

For example, if after assessing your diet you find that your basic fibre intake is just 10g per day, for the next month you need to achieve 15g per day, dividing it into 5g per meal. If after a month on this regime your symptoms are improving, you will need to increase your fibre intake again, this time to 20g per day (that is, about 6–7g per meal). Finally, after another month, you may need to push it up to 24g per day or 8g fibre per meal. What you are looking to achieve is a regular, consistent, predictable bowel movement every day.

Choose your meals according to the healthy meal plate (see page 20) ensuring that the meal is based on complex carbohydrates (see page 18). This will result in a larger percentage of your fibre intake coming from insoluble fibre. Be sure to maintain regular meal times.

Take your total fibre allowance for the day and spread it out into three meals. Use the table on pages 24–25 showing the fibre content of basic foods and the recipes in this book to ensure you are getting approximately the same amount of fibre at each meal. Aim ultimately to achieve 22–28g of fibre per day, depending on your tolerance. Adjust your dose of or wean yourself off any prescribed bulking agent or laxative as your fibre goal is reached.

Rotate your fibre food choices – do not get into the habit of eating the same foods week after week. Research with digestive bran has shown that we develop a type of immunity to one fibre type, so it is best to rotate your fibre choices as often as possible, ensuring a varied diet.

The diarrhoea predominant sufferer

For patients with ongoing diarrhoea the first step is to decrease all fibre or residue in the diet to allow the bowel to rest and regenerate. The low-fibre/residue, low-fat diet (see the table opposite) is one that removes all fibrous substances as well as any food item that leaves residue behind after digestion. Plan your meals using the healthy meal plate, as illustrated on page 20, but stick to the foods on your allowed list. It is extremely difficult to ensure proper nutritional balance on such a restricted diet. Normally diarrhoea ceases after two to three weeks on this diet. If it doesn't you should seek a dietitian's advice to ensure it is safe to continue with the diet and that you are carefully monitored so that no unnecessary deficiencies arise. If the diarrhoea doesn't stop, you may need to start a supervised exclusion diet (see page 31).

You should take a good multivitamin while you are on the low-fibre/residue diet, along with a good-quality probiotic supplement in order to replace lost gut friendly bacteria.

After two or three weeks if the diarrhoea has settled down, you can start reintroducing fibre to your meals. Be cautious as your bowel will be very

The low-fibre/residue, low-fat diet

FOODS ALLOWED	FOODS TO AVOID
White flour and flour products e.g. white bread, rich tea biscuits, wafer biscuits, plain sponge cake, Madeira cake, cream crackers	Brown bread and all wholemeal flour products, wholewheat crispbreads, digestives, and other biscuits, fruit cake, fruit desserts, oatcakes
Toasted rice cereal (e.g. Rice Krispies), corn flakes, cooked and sieved oat porridge	Bran cereals, whole grain wheat cereal (e.g. Shredded Wheat), wheat biscuits (e.g. Weetabix), oatmeal and muesli
White rice and pasta	Brown rice and wholemeal pasta
Fruit juices Stewed or sieved fruit Tender whole tinned fruit	Fresh fruit with skins, pips or seeds All dried fruits
Soft baby carrots Well-cooked vegetables	All raw vegetables, salads, pulses
Clear and well-puréed light soups	Vegetable soups
Peeled potatoes – mashed or boiled	Potatoes with skins – fried, roast, jacket
Lean, tender meat and poultry	Fried and highly seasoned meats, duck, goose, meat products e.g. sausages and meat pies
Boneless fish – grilled or poached	Fried, oily, bony fish e.g. herring, trout, kippers, sardines
250ml low-fat milk per day OR 125ml low-fat milk and 1 small low-fat yogurt Small amounts of plain cheese Eggs Butter and other fats in moderation	Cream, fruit yogurt Fried eggs
Jelly and sorbet	Fruit desserts, ice cream
Sugar, jelly jams and marmalade, honey, syrup	Coarse marmalade, jams with pips or skins
Salt	Pepper, pickles, strongly flavoured spices
Squashes, carbonated drinks	Strong tea and coffee

sensitive and will need a very slow reacquaintance with fibre. Add one new item at a time, distributing the fibre evenly throughout the day within fibre types and meals. IBS patients in this group tend to settle on a lower amount of fibre (18g) than the constipation-predominant types.

The alternating diarrhoea and constipation sufferer

If your symptoms alternate between diarrhoea and constipation, you should approach fibre manipulation in the same way as described for the constipation-predominant sufferer, taking careful note of your symptoms at each step.

If your diarrhoea worsens after slowly increasing your fibre as described above, decrease your fibre intake to under 10g per day for two to four weeks. If things settle down, gradually start increasing it again; then, if there still is no change in your symptoms, consider the non-dietary aspects of your treatment, such as stress management and lifestyle changes.

Try to get all aspects of the treatment in place before making a judgement on how effective the diet is. You may be following the most perfect diet but find that a lack of fluid or a stressful event can cause your symptoms to be the same as before or worse. In other words, get your house in order before judging the effect of the diet.

If everything is in place but symptoms are persisting, it may mean that you need to start the exclusion diet (see page 31).

Wind and bloating

Often IBS sufferers find that once their bowel function is back to normal they are still left with some wind, bloating and sometimes abdominal cramps. There are a number of treatment solutions depending on the cause, the most common of which are outlined below.

1. Too much fibre too soon (that is, more than 30g per day)

IBS sufferers who are keen to see improvement (understandably) will often get going with their new high-fibre diet rather too enthusiastically. If you are not used to fibre in your gut, it is best to start introducing it slowly, increasing it by 5g every four weeks. Sometimes patients return a month later to their doctor for a follow-up visit, full of complaints about experiencing worse symptoms of wind and bloating than they started with. Their immediate assumption is that they must have an intolerance to wheat. On analysis of their food diary it is often obvious that they have far exceeded their fibre prescription and in a very short space of time have even tripled their fibre intake.

The lazy bowel which is not used to fibre tends to react badly to too much too soon. Experience shows that a slow but consistent reintroduction of fibre to a fibre-depleted diet is the most successful course. Small increments of 5g extra fibre per month seem best tolerated. The solution in such cases is either to cut back immediately to a more manageable level of fibre intake, wait until symptoms dissipate and then slowly try to increase your intake of total fibre again, balancing up the fibre types and distribution among meals. Some patients complain that this initial process of building up their fibre intake leaves them with not enough to eat. In such cases try taking in extra food in the form of low-fat refined carbohydrates such as plain biscuits, white bread and crackers.

2. Too much total fibre (that is, more than 30g per day)

There are those who are so keen to increase their fibre intake that they take it way over the top limit of 30g per day without realising it. There seems to be a very fine line between having too little and too much fibre and the latter can cause excessive bowel movement, bloating and wind. If you have fallen into this trap, decrease your total fibre to a level that is comfortable to produce the best and most satisfying bowel habit.

3. Too much soluble fibre

A high intake of soluble versus insoluble fibre can also lead to excess amounts of food residues available for gut fermentation in the colon. Soluble fibre is metabolised by healthy gut bacteria to produce short chain fatty acids (energy) and gases. In certain people who harbour excessive amounts of sulphur-producing bacteria, extra gases such as hydrogen sulphide and methanethiol are also produced, which result in bad smelly wind. The short chain fatty acids feed the colonic bacteria, increasing their quantity and fermentation rate and so producing an increase in bowel gases.

It is a common error, when attempting to increase your fibre intake, to be over-enthusiastic and eat too great a quantity of fruit, vegetables, pulses, nuts and seeds, which are the main sources of soluble fibre in our diet. In order to achieve the right balance, aim to maintain but not exceed the recommended five portions of fruit and vegetables per day and ensure that all starch portions in your meals are those which contain insoluble fibre. Do not make the mistake of counting oats as an insoluble source when they are actually classified as a soluble fibre (see page 22). Be aware, too, of the perils of the smoothie revolution. Smoothies are healthy drinks in that they do contain massive amounts of vitamins, but they also contribute a large load of soluble fibre which you don't necessarily need.

4. Bacterial overgrowth

Bacterial overgrowth can occur as a result of an excessive intake of soluble fibre, as discussed above, resulting in an increase in the number of bacteria in the bowel and subsequent increases in colonic gas production.

Moreover, the value of probiotics (see page 34) for the IBS patient has not yet been clearly established. They have been shown to benefit sufferers from post-infective type IBS, but for the time being we still need to be conscious that too much of a 'good' thing can also be bad.

If we load our bowel with excesses of these good bacteria, are we not supplying more bacteria to ferment available food residues and so produce even more gas?

5. 'Windy' foods

Certain foods, particularly those from the brassica plant family (such as cabbages and brussels sprouts) are notorious for producing windy bowels, probably due to the sulphur-containing compounds found in many of them. A very basic list of other possible culprit foods is given below. There is no need to avoid them all; instead, keep the list on the fridge and when you experience a very bad bout of abdominal wind, check the list to see if you have eaten any of these foods.

Foods and drinks that have been associated with an increased production of intestinal wind

Fish	Asparagus
Milk products	Garlic
Dried beans	Sweet potatoes
Cucumbers	Sweetcorn
Mushrooms	Yeast
Onions	Melons
Brussels sprouts	Nuts
Peas	Sugar
Spinach	Sweets
Cabbage	
Broccoli	Fizzy drinks
Radishes	Sweetened drinks
Cauliflower	Beer

Practical tips to increase your fibre intake

▸ Ensure that all the starch or grains that you eat are the high-fibre varieties. Read the labels of cereals and breads to check.

▸ Switch to wholegrain breads (which should contain at least 2–3g of fibre per slice).

▸ Introduce more wholegrains, such as wholemeal pasta and brown rice, into your main meal.

▸ Have three servings of fruit and two of vegetables per day, where possible raw and with their skins, pips and membranes. Start the day by including a piece of fresh fruit in your breakfast, have fruit as a dessert in your main meal and as a between-meal snack.

▸ Don't forget the fluid. Without fluid, dietary fibre cannot do its job. Drink at least 1.5–2 litres (2¾–3½ pints) per day. Suitable fluids include all non-caffeine and non-alcohol-based fluids like water, herbal teas, well-diluted fruit juices and fruit squashes.

▸ If you need to snack, choose high-fibre options, such as dried fruit, nuts and raisins, wholemeal biscuits and rusks, popcorn.

▸ Try to include cooked beans, peas or lentils as part of your main meal.

▸ Avoid processed, pre-prepared foods: they have a lower fibre content than their fresh alternatives.

Food intolerance and food exclusion

From the above dietary prescriptions and comments you will note that eliminating any item of food from your diet should be the absolute last resort. All too often patients eliminate important nutrients without fully investigating the causes of their actions. True food allergy/intolerance is in fact very rare. Many people end up developing what we refer to as a perceived food intolerance, where their brain-gut axis is very much involved, and although these people do not have a real intolerance, because of what they have read and how certain circumstances have evolved, they react as if they are actually intolerant. It is a challenge for the doctors and dietitians involved in their care to gain their trust to try these eliminated food items again.

Foods which seem most likely to cause true allergenic reactions are dairy products, coffee, wheat, eggs, corn, potatoes, onions, citrus fruit and yeasts. An exclusion diet involves eating only a few foods or a low allergenic diet for a few weeks and then slowly introducing one new food at a time, taking careful note of your symptoms along the way. It is a long, drawn-out process that often reveals quite inconclusive results.

Any attempt to eliminate these 'suspect' foods from your diet should be done only under proper supervision by a state-registered dietitian when all other avenues of IBS treatment have been exhausted.

Weight gain and the high-fibre diet

Maintaining and/or losing weight are major concerns for many of us. Often, when people are faced with the concept of eating more carbohydrate, panic sets in. The reason is that when eating this way you will find that you are consuming larger volumes of food. Complex carbohydrate is bulky and it seems bigger on your plate. The aim is to achieve a bulkier diet to get your bowels moving more consistently. However, high-fibre foods, provided they are prepared in a healthy low-fat manner, will not increase your calorie intake, and some people, who up to now have been eating a high-fat diet, will see their calorie intake actually decrease. Rest assured that this way of eating will make your bowel function better and could even result in some weight loss.

What About Fluid?

We are all aware that we need to drink suitable amounts of fluid, but how vital is it and how many of us actually do it? Taking too little of the right fluid and too much of the wrong fluid can be disastrous for your health. It is all too easy to let the whole day pass without having enough fluid.

The human body is made up on average of 50 per cent water. If you are an athlete, this can go up to 60 per cent. If you are overweight, the figure drops to around 40 per cent. This is because lean muscle tissue contains more water than fat tissue. About two-thirds of the water in the body is contained in cells; the other third travels around the body in blood and body fluids. In an average male this third can be equivalent to 14 litres (3 gallons) of fluid.

A normal healthy person loses water all the time through evaporation from the skin, lungs, urine and faeces. Lost volumes can total up to 2.6 litres (4½ pints) per day, so provision of sufficient fluids ensures an optimal internal environment for regulating digestion, absorption, metabolism and excretion. A loss or decrease in body fluids lessens the efficiency of the mechanisms at work within your body, preventing the major organs from working at their most efficient rate.

Continuous mild dehydration can also result in:

▶ **Constipation**. Fluid is vital for softening the fibre eaten in order to prevent constipation. Too little fluid will result in hard stools that are difficult to pass. Without fluid, dietary fibre cannot do its job. Insoluble fibre in particular acts like a sponge absorbing water, increasing stool weight and size, thus putting pressure on the bowel wall and facilitating movement of the stool. Without fluid this fibre is pointless and will only constipate you further.

▶ **Cystitis**. Too little fluid provides an environment in the bladder that encourages unhealthy bacteria. Increased fluid intake will provide a healthy flow through the bladder, preventing any accumulation of unhealthy bacteria.

▶ **Dehydration**. Symptoms of lethargy, headaches and generally feeling off colour are signs of mild dehydration, though not easily recognised as such. Excessive alcohol intake can also lead to dehydration.

When fluid is lost from your body, the concentration of salt in the blood rises, causing the mechanism of thirst to be activated. However, don't assume that you are drinking enough just because you are not thirsty. As we get older our ability to detect thirst diminishes.

We can obtain water for our bodies from both the fluid we drink and the food we eat. Although the recommendation is to drink 1.5–2 litres (2¾–3½ pints) per day, this is only a guideline and fluid needs are rather individual. They depend on your body size and structure, level of fitness and dietary factors such as your caffeine and alcohol intake.

The best monitor is the colour of your urine and the frequency of urination. Urine that is pale yellow and frequent is a good sign that plenty of fluid is available for waste excretion. Bright yellow urine is an indication of a dehydrated body. (Note, however, that vitamin B supplementation can cause urine to become dark yellow in colour.)

What to drink?
Water and watery drinks

Water is the best option. You may wish to drink bottled spring or mineral water, still or sparkling. Have what you like best, because that will ensure you drink the biggest volume. There is nothing wrong with tap water, and in many cases tap water is subject to more regulations regarding purity than bottled water. Some bottled water is fortified with minerals such as calcium and magnesium. If you live in a hard-water area, check the mineral content of your tap water with your supplier – you may be surprised to learn that it has a higher mineral content than that of bottled water.

Fruit juice and fruit squashes come next, but dilute them to the maximum as their sugar content can be high.

Try also herbal and fruit teas, but be wary of green teas as most varieties are rather high in caffeine.

Keep carbonated drinks to a minimum (not more than one a day) as they are high in sugar and additives.

Caffeine

Most of us eat caffeine-rich foods such as chocolate and drink caffeine-rich fluids. Caffeine stimulates the heart and central nervous system and acts within our bodies in the same way as amphetamines, cocaine and heroin. It is therefore addictive and dehydrating. If you feel you cannot function without it, you are addicted to caffeine. Some people consume up to 1000mg per day, equivalent to ten cups of percolated coffee or 15 cups of instant coffee. How much do you drink? Try to limit your intake of caffeine-rich fluids to no more than three drinks per day.

Alcohol

Be sensible about your alcohol consumption. Remember that alcohol has a diuretic effect, thus promoting an increase in normal fluid losses. In order for the body to process the dehydrating effects of one glass of wine, it will need the equivalent in water over and above your normal fluid intake. Don't forget that alcohol is very calorie-dense but nutrient-deficient, so replacing meals with alcohol on too many occasions can lead to nutritional deficiencies.

Sensible alcohol intakes

Men: 3–4 units per day or less
Women: 2–3 units per day or less
Have three alcohol-free days a week
1 unit =
½ pint of beer or
1 small glass of sherry or
1 small glass of wine or
1 single measure of spirits

Good alcohol habits to create

▶ Eat first, then drink alcohol.
▶ Alternate water and alcohol.
▶ Try low-alcohol or non-alcoholic drinks.
▶ Add low-calorie mixers to extend your drinks.
▶ Drink slowly, take small sips and pace yourself.
▶ After a bad drinking binge, give your body a 48-hour rest.

Good reasons to increase your fluid intake:
▶ Gets your body in motion.
▶ Avoids constipation.
▶ Increases nutrient absorption.
▶ Moisturises your skin.
▶ Keeps your kidneys healthy.
▶ Decreases muscle cramps.
▶ Prevents kidney stones.
▶ Avoids dehydration.
▶ Regulates your body temperature.

Tips to help you drink more:
▶ Start drinking early in the day.
▶ Drink small amounts throughout the day.
▶ Have a bottle of water on your desk, in your car and in your briefcase.
▶ Drink while travelling.
▶ Drink while exercising.
▶ Decrease the amount of tea, coffee and alcohol you drink, create a thirst and replace it with water.
▶ Put a reminder on the screensaver on your computer.
▶ Try warm water.
▶ Try flavouring water with slices of fresh fruit.

Caffeine content of what you drink and eat	
Coffee rng per 190g cup	
Instant	61–70
Percolated	97–125
Tea mg per 190g cup	15–75
Cocoa mg per 190g cup	10–17
Chocolate (per 65g milk chocolate)	60–70
Cola drinks mg per 343g can	43–65
Some sports drinks mg per 330g can	18
Performance Alert drinks mg per 250g can	75

The Alternative Side

Probiotics, prebiotics and symbiotics

Recently there has been a flood of 'fermented', 'live' or 'bio' products on our supermarket shelves, most of these based on dairy products. The processes of regulating our gut bacteria can be defined as three separate approaches:

▶ Probiotics
▶ Prebiotics
▶ Symbiotics

Probiotics are live microbial food supplements, widely used in 'live' yogurts and dairy products. Best known are the lactic acid bacteria and bifidobacteria.

More recently and not as extensively marketed or researched are another group of foodstuffs known as the prebiotics. These are defined as non-digestible foodstuffs which pass through the bowel, arriving in the colon undigested. Here they are said to be selectively able to stimulate the growth of the above-mentioned probiotics. The group of carbohydrates called the oligosaccharides (a type of dietary fibre) is the best known of these.

This brings us to symbiotics, the third possibility of gut bacteria management. This involves the proposed interaction between certain probiotics and prebiotics in order to improve the survival of the probiotic and thus prolong its said benefits.

'Bio' and 'live' products promise to boost the body's natural resistance, promote healthy digestion and improve the balance of our own gut microflora through the addition of probiotic bacteria. There is little, but growing, hard scientific evidence investigating the mechanisms and processes involved in this probiotic phenomenon. Indeed, probiotics do have a significant potential for improving human health and preventing and treating disease. Probiotic supplementation has, however, been seen to be beneficial in treating those with post-infective IBS by replacing valuable gut bacteria.

Lactose intolerance

One of the most common groups of foods avoided by IBS sufferers is milk and other dairy products. In a desperate attempt to find their own solution some IBS patients start eliminating lactose from their diet. When we adopt such a course of action, unfortunately we are often doing more harm than good.

What we do know is that lactose malabsorption may induce symptoms indistinguishable from certain variants of IBS, particularly the diarrhoea-predominant type, such as nausea, abdominal discomfort, cramps, bloating and diarrhoea. These symptoms in lactose intolerance are brought about by fermentation of lactose in the intestine. It is easily seen how the two conditions can be confused and therefore it is strongly recommended that lactose malabsorption be properly excluded by your doctor before the diagnosis of IBS is made.

There is, however, a certain percentage of IBS patients who do have true lactose intolerance. The available research is very varied in terms of its conclusiveness as to the real incidence in IBS patients, but it does seem certain that some may well be lactose intolerant. It is just not nearly as many of you as you think. The best advice is not to self-diagnose. If you suspect that you may be intolerant to dairy products, seek your answer from the professionals. A physician will run a lactose-tolerance test, and if a positive diagnosis is made, it will be followed up with an appointment with a qualified dietitian to ensure that what needs to be eliminated from your diet will be replaced with suitable substitutes.

Sorbitol

Sorbitol is an artificial sweetener used in slimming foods, soft drinks and diabetic foods. Large doses of sorbitol or fructose-sorbitol mixtures have been seen to worsen or induce diarrhoea in adults.

Peppermint

Peppermint is a natural anti-spasmodic that relaxes the muscles that line the bowel wall. Many doctors prescribe it as a first line of treatment. Study results have not been consistently positive, but if you would like to try peppermint, be sure to use enteric-coated capsules, which will only dissolve lower down in the gut and will not cause or aggravate heartburn. Peppermint tea has a milder effect than the tablets.

Aloe vera

In some cases patients have reported that aloe vera has been beneficial in reducing IBS symptoms. Although there is no clear evidence to support its use, anecdotal evidence does suggest that aloe vera may ease discomfort by an anti-inflammatory and possibly immune-enhancing effect. It is available from health food stores and is most often taken in liquid form by adding 2 teaspoons to a glass of water.

Vegetarianism and IBS

Many vegetarians are not following a healthy balanced vegetarian diet. They have eliminated certain protein foods for whatever reason and not replaced them with suitable substitutes, resulting in a poorly balanced diet. However a carefully planned vegetarian diet generally corresponds very closely to healthy eating ideals in terms of fat, carbohydrate and fibre content. This type of diet tends to be low in saturated fat, cholesterol and animal protein and contains increasing concentrations of folate, antioxidants (vitamins C and E, carotinoids and phytochemicals) and complex carbohydrates and fibre, all of which offer certain disease protection. Epidemiological studies have shown that vegetarians have a lower body weight, lower blood fat levels and therefore decreased incidence of coronary heart disease.

Vegetarians also suffer less hypertension (high blood pressure) and a lower risk of the complications arising from diabetes. This is perhaps due to their increased intake of fibre-rich foods and decreased body mass index (weight to height ratio). The incidence of lung, breast and colon cancer is also less in vegetarians. It has been seen that the colon of a vegetarian differs greatly from that of a non-vegetarian and of course this definitely should have implications for the IBS patient.

Most vegetarian diets have a fibre intake that meets or exceeds the recommended dietary allowance (RDA) of 24g. The very fine line between having too much and too little fibre was explained earlier in this book. It is also important to ensure that you get the fibre ratio right, the largest percentage of your fibre intake coming from insoluble sources (such as cereals, breads, rice, pasta and so on). In the vegetarian diet there is the advantage that the diet is naturally high in fibre, but can easily be too high, especially in soluble fibre (found in fruit, vegetables, pulses and nuts). This will result in a worsening of IBS symptoms, with added bloating, wind, abdominal pain and possibly diarrhoea.

Shopping and Eating Out

Changing to this way of eating might mean a whole new way of shopping. We all tend to charge through the supermarket at a rapid pace, grabbing those same old things we always buy, so you will need to put a little time aside to cruise the aisles and stock up on some good high-fibre essential ingredients. Before you do that, you need to know what to choose and how to read labels.

Reading labels

We are lucky that food labelling is so well regulated these days. If you can understand what you are reading, this information is very useful in helping you plan your diet.

First, ingredients are listed in order of their weight content in that particular food, with the largest at the beginning. This information can be of use to people allergic to or avoiding certain foods – for example, sugars or gluten containing products.

The nutritional content of a product is what an IBS patient really needs to look at. The most commonly listed nutrients are energy, protein, carbohydrate, sugar, fat, (including saturates), fibre and sodium. Nutrients are listed per 100g of the product and also per manufacturer's recommended portion size. Here it is important to check if you are eating the same portion size; if not, you will have to recalculate to get an accurate idea of what you are consuming.

There is some controversy yet to be resolved regarding the labelled fibre content of foods. Expert opinion in the UK believes that the Englyst method of fibre analysis (see page 6) should be the preferred one, but many other countries favour the American Organisation of Analytical Chemists (AOAC) method, which results in a higher estimate of fibre content. The fibre content of various foods given in this book is based on the Englyst method. Food products packaged in the UK are labelled in this way as well. However, some manufacturers give two fibre analyses on their packaging – one according to each method.

The guideline daily amounts (GDAs) are listed on most packages to help you, the consumer, calculate how that given product would fit into a normal healthy diet for an adult of normal body weight. These are shown in the table to the right. So if you are choosing a product that is high in fat, perhaps a cheesy pasta dish, that uses up half your fat allowance for the day, you will be able to calculate how much fat you have 'left' and know to choose lower-fat options from then on. Remember: these are meant only as a guideline, since needs vary from one person to another.

The 'little and a lot' table, also shown above, has been devised to help you judge how much of a particular ingredient a food contains. It is useful when comparing one product with another and will help you determine if what you are buying is high enough in fibre and low enough in fat to meet your dietary requirements.

Nutritional guidelines

A LOT	A LITTLE
20g fat	3g fat
5g saturates	1g saturates
3g fibre	0.5g fibre
10g sugars	2g sugars
0.5g sodium	0.1g sodium

If you want to know the amount of salt (sodium chloride) in a product, multiply the sodium by 2.5.

Guideline daily amounts

	MEN	WOMEN
Energy	2500 kcals	2000 kcals
Fat	95g	70g
Saturates	30g	20g
Fibre	20g	16g
Sugar	70g	50g
Sodium	2.5g	2g

Choosing fresh foods

Obviously you need plenty of fresh fruit and vegetables. Use your lists and choose lots of high-fibre fruit and vegetables such as pears, oranges, apples, berries, spinach, broccoli, carrots, sprouts, sweetcorn and so on. Vary your choice from shop to shop, and try things you don't normally buy.

Visit the bakery and get some freshly baked wholemeal grainy bread, then add some wholemeal pitta bread, pumpernickel and wholemeal muffins to your shopping basket. If you are following a low-fibre diet, go for refined, soft white breads.

Choosing store-cupboard foods

Cereals and grains

Supermarket shelves are stocked with a wide range of high-fibre cereals. Read the labels and choose those that are low in fat and sugar but that meet your fibre requirements. Breakfast cereals are versatile in that they can be used in baked goods, as toppings or bases, or as an extender in meat dishes like meatballs. Wheat bran and rice bran are good sources of fibre to keep at hand to add to baked goods, desserts and cereals to boost the insoluble fibre content.

Pulses

Buy dried beans, peas, lentils, chickpeas and so on in their dried or tinned form. Tinned pulses are easier to use as there is no need to soak and boil them – just open the can, rinse in water and add them to salads, vegetables, meat dishes and soups.

Rice and pasta

Try brown rice, wild rice, red rice and brown basmati rice, which all contain considerably more fibre than white rice.

Wholemeal pasta is a really good source of insoluble fibre, but it may contain too much fibre for your specific requirement, in which case mix it with white pasta to get used to the flavour and to build up your fibre intake. Spelt or faro pasta, which is used in some of the recipes in this book, is an excellent source of fibre and people often find it more acceptable in taste than the really nutty wholemeal pastas.

Biscuits and crackers

Choose wholemeal, oat and rye-based crackers and biscuits, which are excellent for snacking on. Also keep a supply of digestive-type biscuits for that sweet-tooth moment.

Dried fruit, nuts and seeds

Keep a good variety of dried fruit, nuts and seeds at home and at work. They are excellent snack foods as a very small quantity will contribute significant amounts of soluble fibre to your diet. They can also be easily added to vegetable dishes, used as a coating, and added to salads, desserts and breakfast cereals when you have run out of fresh fruit.

Eating out

It is unreasonable to assume that you won't occasionally want fast foods or a nice meal in a restaurant. Don't avoid eating out because of this diet: it has to fit in with your lifestyle and life has to go on. Remember that when your eating plan is established, as long as you keep to it most of the time, the odd meal where you disregard the rules is not going to make that much of a difference to your symptoms. In time you will also find a few favourite restaurants where you know you can get a delicious meal that also meets your dietary requirements. It is

possible to get sufficient amounts of fibre in some restaurants (such as French-style, Mexican, Eastern, English pubs, American steak houses or Italian). In others (Indian and burger bars) it is not that easy.

Quick tips for eating out

▶ If you will be eating in a restaurant where you know you will not get all the components required in your diet, a good way of taking the pressure off yourself (and to make sure that you enjoy the outing more) is to have a decent high-fibre snack before you go out – for example two rye crispbreads, a pear, a handful of nuts or some dried fruit. Then, at the restaurant, skip the starch option and just have the meat, fish or chicken and the vegetables.

▶ Alternatively take some wholemeal or brown bread from the basket and have that instead of the low-fibre rice that may be on offer.

▶ Always make sure you get some extra vegetables and/or salad with your main course.

▶ Choose the lowest-fat option that you can.

▶ Choose fruity desserts.

▶ If you drink wine or other alcohol, drink double the amount of water as well.

▶ Try not to overeat, even though the food tastes good.

▶ Try not to eat out too late in the evening.

French

Although sometimes served in smaller portions than you may be used to, this type of eating is in most cases reasonably healthy in terms of fat content but often rather lacking in insoluble-fibre options. It may be better to have your starch for the evening before you go out, in the form of a high fibre cracker type snack, then when you are at the restaurant you can concentrate on the beautifully prepared vegetables and protein dishes.

Mexican

The pulse content of Mexican meals makes them worthwhile for people on a high-fibre diet. Be wary, though, of the fat content of some menu items such as enchiladas, guacamole, sour cream and fried tortilla. Rather, go for fajitas, vegetable dishes or bean, chickpea and pulse dishes. Stay away from anything too spicy: it will aggravate the lining of your bowel wall and could worsen your symptoms.

Eastern

Here the noodles are a slightly better choice than the rice dishes, as they contain more fibre, but stick to the boiled and steamed options (not the fried noodles) for keeping your fat intake down. Vegetables, nuts and seeds are plentiful in this type of cooking for good soluble-fibre content. Choose wisely to keep your fat down and your fibre up. Be cautious of the spicy dishes if these tend to worsen your symptoms.

English pub meals

Try a jacket potato with a low-fat sauce like bolognaise, tuna or perhaps some baked beans if you are looking for more fibre. Grilled fish with new potatoes and the vegetables of the day is a good option, or try a salad combined with some chunky high-fibre bread (watch out for the dressing, though).

American steak houses

This steak meal is quite a good choice mainly because you can control it all. You can order the size steak you want and choose your accompaniments, such as jacket or new potatoes. Steak portions tend to be large but try to stick to 125g–150g (4½–5oz) maximum. Salads are normally available from a salad bar, which is just perfect for allowing you to control what you get. So you can end up with a really well-balanced meal that is high in fibre.

Italian

Choose pasta in preference to pizza – it has a fibre content worth counting, and is not nearly as high in fat as the average pizza. Also remember to go for tomato-based vegetable sauces rather than the creamy, cheesy, high-fat ones. Have a salad to start, with dressing on the side so that you can control the amount added.

Indian

It is hard to get suitable fibre in an Indian restaurant – rice, poppadums and meat curries will not satisfy your fibre needs. You could go for the lentil, pulse-based and vegetable curries, which will give you some soluble fibre. Perhaps have very little of the starch on offer and top up with a few high-fibre crackers when you get home. You will need to go for mildly flavoured dishes rather than anything too hot and spicy. What tastes good now could cause irritation to your bowel tomorrow. Keep the fat down by choosing dry curries and tomato-based sauces like jalfrezi and rogan josh.

Fast food

Burgers and fried chicken are no good in any format, so don't go there.

Fish and chips are full of fat, and the only way you could get (soluble) fibre would be to have some baked beans or mushy peas with them.

Other takeaway meals are covered by the information on various types of cuisine given above and on page 39.

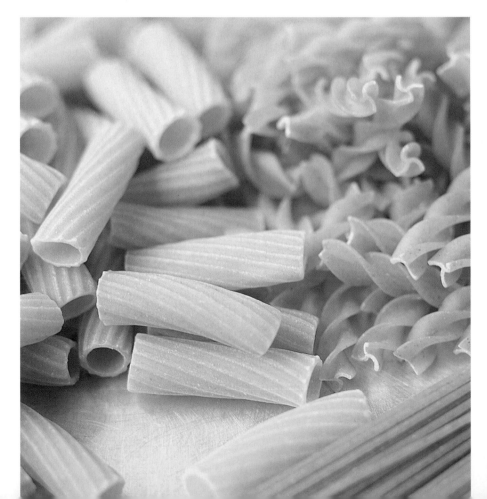

How to Use this Book

As we have seen, IBS is a complex condition and many factors are involved. We know that the best results in treatment are achieved when all aspects of the treatment are dealt with. Take some time to make sure you understand all the issues discussed so far, and put the following points into practice:

▸ Address lifestyle factors such as stress, relaxation and exercise
▸ Assess your current diet
▸ Ensure you are meeting healthy eating guidelines
▸ Put good eating habits into place
▸ Ensure you are drinking enough fluids

Once these factors are in place, you can determine the amount of fibre that is right for you by identifying which type of IBS you have and how much fibre you currently have in your diet. You will have already determined whether you have low, medium or high levels of fibre in your diet as follows (see page 23):

Low fibre	0–12g per day
Medium fibre	12–18g per day
High fibre	18–25g per day

You will also have decided which of the following best describes your bowel function:

▸ Constipation predominant sufferer
▸ Diarrhoea predominant sufferer
▸ Alternating constipation and diarrhoea sufferer

Pages 22–23 explain how to manipulate your fibre intake according to which group you fall into. To help you achieve the fibre levels that are right for you, the recipes in this book are categorised as low, medium or high fibre and are defined as follows:

LOW	0–3g fibre per meal
MEDIUM	3–5g fibre per meal
HIGH	5–8g fibre per meal

These will help you to reach your low, medium or high fibre targets per day as shown above. You will also need to account for accompaniments and snacks.

You can move between low, medium and high levels of fibre as needed by referring to the nutritional breakdown of each recipe. You can also adapt recipes to higher or lower levels of fibre by serving them with different accompaniments or omitting certain ingredients; see the tips in the recipe introductions. The recipes in the Meat and Fish chapters are mostly classed as low fibre, because meat and fish are in themselves not fibrous, but you can make these meals higher in fibre by serving with wholemeal bread, brown rice noodles, potatoes or other vegetable or fruit accompaniments. Choose appropriately by referring to their labels and the fibre table on pages 24–25.

The sample menu planners on pages 42–43 give you an idea of how you might plan your meals according to whether you are following a low residue diet or low, medium or high fibre diet.

You will soon become familiar with the fibre content of different foods and once you become adept at reading food labels, choosing foods with the right level of fibre for you will become second nature.

Always remember to approach the management of your IBS from a holistic perspective encompassing all the lifestyle factors as well as dietary factors dealt with in this book. Most of all remember to enjoy your food!

Sample Menus

LOW RESIDUE

	DAY 1	DAY 2	DAY 3
Breakfast	Toasted rice cereal (e.g. Rice Krispies) with semi-skimmed milk Fresh fruit juice	White toast with olive-oil based margarine and honey Yogurt and stewed apples	Boiled egg, grilled tomato and white toast Fresh fruit juice
Lunch	Asparagus and Potato Fritatta (page 74) White bread roll Baked apple (no skin) with honey and low-fat crème fraîche	Wild Mushroom and Tomato Soup (page 61) White crispbreads with a little cheese Fresh fruit juice	Sandwich with roasted vegetables and lean ham, made with crusty white farmhouse bread Puréed berry fruit coulis and yogurt
Dinner	Garam Masala Duck Breast (page 98) Boiled peeled potatoes Steamed vegetables Almond and Polenta Biscuits (page 137) with stewed fruit (not fresh)	Baked Fish Parcel (page 88) Savoury rice Stir-fried Asparagus with Sesame Seeds (page 108) Peach and Grappa Sorbet (page 134)	Oriental Steamed Tofu with Mushrooms and Greens (page 112) Cherry tomatoes Steamed noodles Tinned peaches and yogurt with honey

LOW FIBRE (12g per day)

	DAY 1	DAY 2	DAY 3
Breakfast 4g	Beef and Potato Hash (page 48) Poached egg Sliced nectarine with skin	Shreddies with semi-skimmed milk Apple	Healthy Eggs Florentine with wholemeal bread (page 51) Banana
Lunch 4g	Grilled sea bass or other white fish Tabbouleh (page 65) Fruit salad	Brown bread sandwich with smoked salmon and salad Grated apple (with skin) and yogurt	Wild Mushroom and Bread Salad (page 66) Wild rocket salad Grapes
Dinner 4g	Meatballs with Chickpeas (page 101) Warm white pitta bread Raspberries and crème fraîche	Grilled Swordfish with Cannellini Bean Salad (page 92) White rice, green salad Strawberry Cheesecake (page 134)	Mediterranean Chicken and Prune Stew (page 104) Wholesome Mashed Tatties in their Skins (page 118) Steamed courgettes and leeks Almond and Polenta Biscuits (page 137) with ice cream (not fresh fruit)

MEDIUM FIBRE (18g per day)

	DAY 1	DAY 2	DAY 3
Breakfast 6g	Apricot Muffin (page 52) Fresh fruit salad with nuts and yogurt	Kedgeree (page 51) ½ grapefruit	Wheat biscuits (e.g. Weetabix) with semi-skimmed milk Fruit juice
Lunch 6g	Bruschetta with Chard, Borlotti Beans and Anchovy Sauce (page 78) Apple	Warm Potato Salad with Green Beans, Spring Onions and Chives (page 67) Grilled chicken breast Fresh orange	Shrimps on Toast (page 79) Fresh fruit salad
Dinner 6g	Persian Chicken with Rice (page 100) Green salad Strawberry Cheesecake (page 134)	Thai Noodles with Tofu and Vegetables (page 112) Tofu-sesame Dipping Sauce with Steamed Vegetables (page 116) Grapes	Grilled Swordfish with Cannellini Bean Salad (page 92) New potatoes Stir-fried Asparagus with Sesame Seeds (page 108) Peach and Grappa Sorbet (page 134)

HIGH FIBRE (24g per day)

	DAY 1	DAY 2	DAY 3
Breakfast 8g	Muesli (page 54) with semi-skimmed milk	Fruit Compote (page 54) with yogurt and a little All-Bran	Wholemeal toast with poached egg, grilled bacon and tomato Melon
Lunch 8g	Rye bread with walnuts, prunes, ricotta and roasted peppers Nectarine	Tuna Niçoise with a Pulse (page 94) Banana	Potato Galette with Wholemeal Pastry (page 81) Green salad Fresh fruit salad
Dinner 8g	Grilled Polenta with Prawns, Venetian Style (page 95) Blackcurrant Fool (page 138)	Grilled Trout with Almonds (page 84) Couscous Grilled Aubergines with Miso (page 116) Chocolate Fridge Cake (page 137)	Middle Eastern Lamb Wrapped in Cabbage Leaves (page 103) Green leafy salad Date-filled Sticky Toffee Pudding (page 140)

I have written several healthy cookery books and have realised how much it has affected the way I shop and cook for my family. When I worked in restaurants I would rarely cook at home. On the few occasions when I would dust off my saucepans and entertain, my menus were often elaborate and full of rich ingredients. Until I started to think about healthy food, I would often pop a carton of cream in my shopping trolley and wouldn't bat an eyelid about pouring copious amounts of olive oil on any dish I was serving. Now I think differently and have felt a great deal better for it.

What I hope to have achieved with this book is to provide you with a variety of recipes to cook at home. Some are elaborate and could be used for entertaining; others are simple ideas for everyday cooking. With a family of my own I know the importance of cooking healthy, but easy dishes that everyone can enjoy. These recipes are not meant to be dull and uninspiring. I wanted to show the reader that stylish and interesting recipes could also be healthy too.

While researching for this book I would often receive lots of chuckles and winks when explaining which book I was working on. I live in Wimbledon and would joke that the title could have been 'Windless from Wimbledon'. IBS is not something many people feel comfortable about discussing. But I was amazed by how many people were interested in the book for themselves or friends and family who suffered from it. In fact, my husband was more than happy to eat the recipes I tested and could verify the effectiveness of them. He looks forward to the sequel!

The other crucial point to make about this book is how much our diet affects this illness. A recipe book is therefore essential to help any person with IBS. This book will give you information and regimes to help keep this ailment at bay, so you can live more of a normal life.

During my research and discussions with Erica, I soon realised there was a disparity between what people perceived they could eat if they suffered from IBS and what was beneficial to them. The list of foods that people wrote down that helped and hindered was often littered with similar food items. But once Erica had explained the complexity of this illness it became apparent that there are no straightforward symptoms. It can vary from day to day; one minute you are constipated, the next minute the opposite.

So the book needed recipes that offered different levels of fibre, depending on what state your bowels were in. Hence the recipes in this book have a low-, medium- or high-fibre rating. This way you can pick and choose which recipe works for your ailments at any given time. I have then, as much as possible, given suggestions for adapting each recipe, so that you can change from low to medium to high accordingly, thus increasing the amount of recipes you can use.

The next point I learnt was that in order to make an effective recovery you could not do it in a hurry. You have to slowly adapt your bowels to a healthy rhythm and it's the maintenance of a healthy rhythm that is important. You could almost describe IBS as a freestyle jazz piece as opposed to a gentle Mozart concerto (no offence to jazz intended!). But a top-performing digestive system needs to be trained and many IBS sufferers have a badly behaved delinquent inside them, not a controlled disciplined athlete. This book will help you tame the beast inside!

Breakfasts and Breads

1

Beef and potato hash
This dish incorporates the Pot-roasted Beef Brisket recipe on page 100, so if you have some left over use it in this recipe to make a delicious breakfast or brunch. Lovely and satisfying, especially on cold winter mornings, or as a weekend treat. **Serves 6**

400–500g (14–18oz) pot-roasted beef brisket (see page 100)
800g (1¾lb) potatoes (waxy or baking depending on how fluffy you like your hash)
8 tablespoons sunflower oil
1 large red onion, coarsely chopped
Salt and freshly ground black pepper
1 large yellow pepper, deseeded and cut into cubes
1 large ripe tomato or 8 cherry tomatoes
Chopped flat-leaf parsley (optional)

Cook the Pot-roasted Beef Brisket according to the recipe on page 100. Remove the meat from the liquid and leave to cool, then flake 400–500g (14–18oz) into chunks (you can use the rest of the meat another day).

To make the beef hash, cook the potatoes whole in their skins in boiling water with a good pinch of salt for about 20–45 minutes, depending on their size. They should be undercooked rather than overcooked. Cut into large chunks.

In a large frying pan, heat the oil and fry the onion and potatoes until the potatoes are light golden brown, seasoning with salt and pepper. Reduce the heat a little, add the yellow pepper, and cook for another 5 minutes. Then add the tomato(es) and cook until any liquid has been reduced and the pepper is soft. Add the flaked beef and cook over a gentle heat for a further 5–10 minutes to allow the flavours to infuse.

Serve with chopped parsley to add colour, if you wish.

Fibre rating: LOW
Per serving: 2.2g fibre, 350 kcals, 21g fat, 4g saturated fat, 0.55g sodium

Focaccia with potatoes, cherry tomatoes and rosemary
An Italian flatbread which can also be flavoured with chopped herbs, caramelised onions or olives. Sprinkle them into the dimples or fold them into the dough just before baking. **Makes 1 x 1.6kg (3½lb) loaf**

1kg (2¼lb) wholemeal flour
Coarse sea salt and freshly ground black pepper
1 sachet easy active dried yeast
1 teaspoon sugar
650ml (23fl oz) lukewarm water
2 tablespoons extra virgin olive oil, plus a bit extra
400g (14oz) cherry tomatoes
150g (5oz) cooked unpeeled potatoes
Several rosemary sprigs

Put the flour, 2 teaspoons salt, the yeast, sugar, water and 1 tablespoon of the olive oil in a bowl or food processor. Knead for about 5 minutes into a soft and slightly sticky ball. Using your hand, smear a film of oil on top, to stop the dough from drying out. Cover with a tea-towel and leave to prove in a warm place for about 2 hours or until doubled in size.

While the bread is rising, preheat the oven to 190°C/375°F/gas mark 5. Put the tomatoes in a gratin dish with the remaining olive oil, salt and pepper and bake in the oven about 1–1½ hours until all the juices have evaporated and the tomatoes are caramelised. Turn the heat down if the tomatoes are starting to burn.

When the dough has risen, coarsely break up the potatoes into small pieces and fold into the dough. Lightly grease a baking tray with olive oil and spread the dough out to form a round of about 30–40cm (12–18in) diameter. Dot over the tomatoes, smashing them into the bread, and smear any cooking juices from them over the top: this is the tastiest bit. Scatter over the rosemary sprigs and finally season with salt and pepper.

Increase the oven temperature to 200°C/400°F/gas mark 6. Leave the dough to rise again for about 30 minutes, then bake in the oven for about 20 minutes, or until golden brown. As soon as it comes out of the oven, drizzle a little olive oil over it and leave to cool for 10 minutes before serving warm.

Fibre rating: LOW
Per 35g slice: 2.2g fibre, 81 kcals, 1g fat, 0g saturated fat, 0.08g sodium

Healthy eggs florentine
This is a simple and healthy version of an egg dish often found on traditional Italian menus in England. It may be cooked in small individual dishes or one larger gratin dish about 20–25cm (8–10in) across. Alternatively you could use small or medium oven-proof frying pans. **Serves 4**

500g (18oz) spinach, washed and drained
Salt and freshly ground black pepper
100g (3½oz) ricotta cheese
8 large basil leaves, finely chopped (optional)
4 eggs
25g (1oz) Parmesan, grated
4 medium slices warm crusty brown bread

Don't bother to trim the spinach stems unless they are very large and tough. Tear the leaves a bit if they are large, or just buy small-leafed spinach for ease.

In a large saucepan or frying pan, cook the spinach in batches, stirring frequently until it is wilted. Spinach has enough moisture in it not to need extra water. Place in a colander until all the spinach is cooked, then squeeze dry, pressing out any excess water.

Preheat the grill to high. Place the warm spinach leaves in four individual heatproof dishes or one large gratin dish and season with salt and pepper.

Put the ricotta in a bowl and mix with the chopped basil leaves, if using, and season with salt and pepper.

Carefully break the eggs over the spinach without breaking the yolks and dollop the ricotta around the sides with a little on top of the yolks. Scatter over the Parmesan and place under the grill. Cook for 2–4 minutes until the eggs are just set but still soft in the middle.

Serve straight away with the warm bread.

Fibre rating: MEDIUM
Per serving including bread: 4.8g fibre, 262 kcals, 13g fat, 5g saturated fat, 1.02g sodium

Kedgeree
In this version of the Anglo-Indian classic, brown or white basmati rice can be used and the lentils omitted, depending on your fibre needs. The trick to cooking brown rice successfully is to use just enough water. It becomes waterlogged very easily and loses its nutty, light appeal. **Serves 4**

150g (5oz) brown basmati rice
75g (3oz) green or Puy lentils
Pinch of turmeric (optional)
1 medium onion, finely chopped
1 teaspoon ground cumin
1 teaspoon ground coriander
3 tablespoons sunflower oil or 50g (2oz) unsalted butter
310g (11oz) smoked haddock fillet, skinned, and thickly sliced
2 eggs (optional)
15g (½oz) fresh coriander, roughly chopped

Place the rice and lentils in a saucepan and add about 500ml (18fl oz) hot water. Add the tumeric, if using, and give the rice and lentils a good stir. Cover with a lid and bring to the boil, then gently simmer for about 20–25 minutes until the rice is just cooked and the lentils are soft. Remove from the heat and leave with the lid on to steam for 10 minutes. If there is still water left in the pan, cook gently until it has all evaporated.

Cook the onion, cumin and ground coriander in the oil or butter in a large high-sided frying pan or saucepan for about 10 minutes, until soft and translucent. Increase the heat to high, add the haddock and cook for a few minutes. When the haddock is just cooked, push to the side and break the eggs, if using, into the saucepan. Cook the eggs until the whites start to turn solid. Break the yolks to help them cook more quickly. When the eggs are just cooked, briefly stir into the haddock mixture, trying to leave large pieces of egg.

Add the rice and lentils to the haddock mixture with half the chopped coriander. Mix briefly until just incorporated. Return to the heat if not hot enough.

Serve with the remaining chopped coriander, wedges of lemon, buttered toast and chutney.

Fibre rating: MEDIUM
Per serving including eggs, not including serving suggestion: 3g fibre, 414 kcals, 17g fat, 5g saturated fat, 0.61g sodium

Wholemeal soda bread with seeds and grains

Soda bread is quick and easy to make. This version is delicious served with smoked salmon for a decadent breakfast or brunch. It also makes great toast. **Makes 1 x 850g (1¾lb) loaf**

450g (1lb) wholemeal flour or granary flour
50g (2oz) bran
50g (2oz) barley flakes (optional)
100g (3½oz) sunflower or pumpkin seeds (reserve 1 tablespoon for topping if you wish)
2 heaped teaspoons sea salt
1 heaped teaspoon baking powder
1 heaped teaspoon bicarbonate of soda or baking soda
175g (6oz) low-fat plain yogurt
200ml (7fl oz) warm water
Oil, for greasing

Preheat the oven to 190°C/375°F/gas mark 5. Lightly oil a large flat roasting tray and place in the oven.

Place the dry ingredients in a large bowl or in a food processor with a dough hook. Mix briefly, then add the yogurt and water. Mix until well incorporated and knead for a few minutes.

When a firm but slightly sticky lump of dough has formed, shape it into a ball. Scatter over the reserved seeds, if using, or dust with flour. Place on the preheated tray and bake for about 40 minutes, until golden brown. Tap the base to check that it sounds hollow and is cooked through.

Transfer to a wire rack and leave to cool for at least 30 minutes before slicing and eating.

Fibre rating: MEDIUM
Per 40g slice: 3.4g fibre, 110 kcals, 3g fat, 0g saturated fat, 0.3g sodium

Apricot muffins

A tasty breakfast or snack. Other dried fruit can be substituted for the apricots, as well as other fresh fruit such as bananas or papaya. For a lower fibre version use plain flour instead of wholemeal flour. The bran included increases the insoluble fibre content. **Makes 10–12 medium muffins**

75ml (3fl oz) sunflower oil, plus extra for greasing
2 medium eggs
150g (5oz) caster sugar
150g (5oz) low-fat plain yogurt
150g (5oz) wholemeal or plain flour, sifted
50g (2oz) bran
1 heaped teaspoon baking powder
Pinch of baking soda (optional)
75g (3oz) dried apricots, chopped
Pinch of ground ginger and/or cinnamon
2 tablespoons chopped roasted nuts, such as almonds or hazelnuts

Preheat the oven to 190°C/375°F/gas mark 5. Grease 12 muffin moulds with sunflower oil.

Whisk the eggs and sugar together until they double in volume or form a ribbon consistency.

Add the sunflower oil, yogurt, sifted flour, bran, baking powder, baking soda, if using, chopped apricots, ginger and/or cinnamon and half the nuts. Fold the mixture gently until just incorporated (do not beat) and spoon into the muffin moulds, so that it is just level with the top. Scatter over the remaining nuts.

Bake in the oven for about 15 minutes until the mixture is just firm and golden brown. Leave to rest in the tin for 5 minutes. Then turn out on to a wire rack to cool, or eat straight away.

Fibre rating: MEDIUM
Per muffin, with wholemeal flour: 3.9g fibre, 241 kcals, 11g fat, 2g saturated fat, 0.12g sodium

Muesli

There are many good varieties of muesli on the market, but most are high in soluble fibre. This one is high in insoluble fibre. The ingredients here are mostly in a ratio of 1:2, so can easily be increased. Play around with ingredients to suit you; try experimenting with other grains such as quinoa. **Serves 4**

50g (2oz) bran flakes
25g (1oz) oatmeal
25g (1oz) roasted coconut
    flakes
25g (1oz) wheatgerm

50g (2oz) dried chopped
    apricots
25g (1oz) brown rice flakes
25g (1oz) unskinned roasted
    almonds, coarsely chopped

Mix all the ingredients together and store in an airtight container to keep fresh.
Serve with just milk or yogurt, or even Fruit Compote (see right), depending on your fibre requirement.

Fibre rating: HIGH
Per serving: 5g fibre, 195 kcals, 7g fat, 2g saturated fat, 0.11g sodium

Fruit compote

A simple dish to prepare in advance and keep in the fridge for at least two weeks. Serve for breakfast with yogurt as well as some good-quality muesli (see left) that includes nuts. It's also delicious as a healthy pudding.

Serves 4

75g (3oz) dried pineapple
75g (3oz) dried apricots,
    quartered
75g (3oz) dried peaches or
    mango, quartered
75g (3oz) dried cherries or
    cranberries
25g (1oz) raisins or currants
250ml (9fl oz) apple juice or
    water
1 small cinnamon stick
½ vanilla pod

2 pieces preserved stem ginger,
    finely chopped
To serve
200g (7oz) low-fat plain
    yogurt
Good-quality muesli (optional
    – see left)
50g (2oz) blanched almonds,
    coarsely chopped and
    roasted in a medium oven
    for 10 minutes

Place the dried fruits in a saucepan and add the apple juice or water, cinnamon and vanilla. Bring to the boil, then simmer gently for 10 minutes. Add the ginger off the heat and leave to cool.
Store in an airtight container in the fridge and use as needed.
Serve a large spoonful on top of some yogurt or good-quality muesli and chopped nuts for a nourishing breakfast.

Fibre rating: HIGH
Per serving, not including muesli: 6g fibre, 278 kcals, 8g fat, 1g saturated fat, 0.05g sodium

Chickpea flat bread

The Indians use a lot of chickpea (or gram) flour and these are moreish little pancakes to serve with any Indian-style dish or just with a dollop of yogurt and good-quality chutney for a snack. You can buy chickpea flour in health food and Oriental food stores. **Serves 4**

250g (9oz) chickpea flour
2 garlic cloves, finely chopped
1 teaspoon finely grated fresh
  ginger (optional)
2 heaped tablespoons coarsely
  chopped coriander
125g (4½oz) low-fat plain
  yogurt

Large pinch of salt
Sunflower oil, for frying
To serve (optional)
Yogurt, diced tomatoes, thinly
  sliced spring onions or red
  onions, coriander sprigs and
  lime chutney

Place the chickpea flour in a bowl and add the garlic, ginger, if using, coriander, yogurt and salt. Pour in 250ml (9fl oz) water and slowly mix together to form a thick batter without lumps. Add more water if too thick.

Heat a frying pan and lightly grease with sunflower oil. Pour in the chickpea batter, about 1 tablespoon at a time, to form small thin pancakes. Cook the pancakes for 3 minutes on each side until lightly browned. As you cook, set the pancakes aside on a warm plate until you have used up all the batter.

Serve the pancakes with yogurt, tomatoes, onions, coriander sprigs and chutney on top.

Fibre rating: HIGH
Per serving, not including serving suggestion: 6.8g fibre, 216 kcals, 4g fat, 1g saturated fat, 0.33g sodium

Rye bread with figs and walnuts

Like all wheat-free breads, this can seem a little on the heavy side, so substitute half the rye flour with granary flour if you prefer (this will give you similar levels of fibre). Other dried fruit can be used instead of figs if you wish. **Makes 1 x 700g (1½lb) loaf**

500g (18oz) rye flour
75g (3oz) walnut pieces
100g (3½oz) dried figs,
  coarsely chopped
7g (2 teaspoons) dried yeast

1 heaped teaspoon sea salt
1 teaspoon brown sugar
300ml (10fl oz) warm water
Oil, for greasing

Place the dry ingredients in a large bowl, or in a food processor with a dough hook, and mix briefly. Add the water and gently mix into a firm sticky dough that holds its shape.

Place the dough on a lightly greased baking tray, forming a round bread shape. Make a cross on the top with a knife and sprinkle with a little flour. Leave to prove, or increase a little in size, in a warm place for about 1–2 hours.

Preheat the oven to 190°C/375°F/gas mark 5.

Bake the bread in the oven for about 30–45 minutes. Remove from the oven and tap the base to check that it sounds hollow and is cooked.

Transfer to a wire rack and leave to cool for at least 30 minutes before slicing and eating. This bread is also delicious toasted.

Fibre rating: HIGH
Per 2 x 35g slice: 6.9g fibre, 247 kcals, 6g fat, 1g saturated fat, 0.2g sodium

Soups and Salads

2

Minestrone with pearl barley

Italians use pasta, rice, pulses or bread in their minestrone to make it a meal in itself. But you can substitute any pulse, e.g. cannellini or borlotti beans, if you want to increase your fibre intake. Try chard as a change from broccoli if you prefer the look. **Serves 6**

4 tablespoons extra virgin olive oil

50g (2oz) smoked streaky bacon, diced

1 large red onion, finely chopped

2 medium carrots, finely chopped (unpeeled)

2 celery sticks, finely chopped

200g (7oz) green beans, finely chopped

2 large courgettes, finely chopped

1 small head broccoli, divided into small florets

2 garlic cloves, chopped

Salt and freshly ground black pepper

75g (3oz) pearl barley

1 tablespoon chopped thyme

1 litre (1¾ pints) chicken stock or water

Drizzle of extra virgin olive oil or fresh pesto sauce, to serve (optional)

In a heavy-based pan, heat the olive oil over a medium heat and cook the bacon, briefly. Add the onion, followed by the rest of the vegetables, adding each after you have chopped them, starting with the carrots and finishing with the garlic. Stir briefly after each addition. Season with salt and pepper and cook gently for 10 minutes, stirring occasionally.

Add the pearl barley and thyme, mix and cook a further few minutes to coat the barley in oil.

Add the chicken stock or water and simmer gently for about 40 minutes, until all the vegetables are tender and the pearl barley soft.

Serve the soup with a drizzle of extra virgin olive oil or pesto sauce if you like. This soup tastes even better if prepared in advance, giving the flavours a chance to develop.

Fibre rating: MEDIUM
Per serving: 3.9g fibre, 138 kcals, 10g fat, 2g saturated fat, 0.75g sodium

Soba noodle broth with chicken

Use any noodles to suit your tastes or fibre needs. Wholemeal or faro noodles would increase the fibre; buckwheat soba noodles and rice noodles are good options if you are trying to avoid wheat. Beef fillet can replace the chicken if you prefer. **Serves 4**

250g (9oz) buckwheat soba noodles

250g (9oz) chicken breast

Dash of oil, for cooking

600ml (1 pint) chicken stock

12 shiitake mushrooms, quartered or halved depending on size

2 spring onions, sliced at an angle

100g (3½oz) sugar snap peas, halved or baby spinach leaves

1 teaspoon hoisin sauce

4 tablespoons mirin or sherry

4 tablespoons Japanese dark soy sauce

Few coriander sprigs

Cook the noodles in lots of lightly salted water following the manufacturer's instructions; take care not to overcook. Drain, refresh in cold water and place in a bowl. Soba noodles can easily stick together like glue, so handle them carefully and leave some water in the bowl to keep them moist.

Heat a griddle until hot and smear the chicken with a little oil to prevent it sticking. Grill the chicken for about 5 minutes each side or until cooked through. Set aside to rest and slice just before serving.

Have all the prepared vegetable to hand before you start to cook them as they are cooked very quickly.

Bring the stock to the boil and add the mushrooms, hoisin sauce, mirin and soy sauce.

While the stock is coming to the boil again, refresh the noodles in hot or boiling water, drain well and divide among four warmed soup bowls. When the stock boils, quickly add the spring onions and peas or spinach. Remove the stock from the heat and, with a slotted spoon, divide the vegetables between the soup bowls. Scatter over the sliced chicken and finally pour over the stock. Garnish with coriander and serve.

Fibre rating: LOW
Per serving: 1.8g fibre, 358 kcals, 3g fat, 1g saturated fat, 0.72g sodium

Wild mushroom and tomato soup

Mushrooms are a low-fibre vegetable so the fibre in this recipe comes from the bread. It is a traditional Italian soup using dried mushrooms which have a more robust flavour than ordinary mushrooms. Use Italian dried porcini for best results. **Serves 4**

4 tablespoons extra virgin olive oil

1 large red onion, finely chopped

3 celery sticks, finely chopped

2 garlic cloves, finely chopped

3 rosemary sprigs, finely chopped

Salt and freshly ground black pepper

30g (generous 1oz) dried porcini mushrooms, soaked for 15 minutes in just enough hot water to cover

150ml (5fl oz) red or white wine

400g (14oz) tin tomatoes or fresh tomatoes, peeled and cubed

To serve

4 slices sourdough bread (optional)

1 garlic clove, halved (optional)

25g (1oz) Parmesan cheese, grated

Drizzle of extra virgin olive oil (optional)

Heat the olive oil in a saucepan and add the chopped onion and celery. Cook at a gentle simmer for about 15 minutes until they are soft and translucent. Add the garlic and rosemary and cook a minute more. Season with salt and pepper.

Drain the porcini, reserving the soaking liquid, and add to the saucepan, mixing for a few minutes. Add the soaking liquid, discarding any sediment, and pour in the wine. Bring to the boil and cook gently until the liquid has reduced back into the mushrooms.

Add the tomatoes to the pan and simmer gently until they are reduced to a thick sauce. Then add about 500ml (18fl oz) water and simmer gently for another 20 minutes.

Toast the bread and rub with the cut side of the halved garlic clove while still warm. Pour the soup into serving bowls, scatter with Parmesan, drizzle a little extra virgin olive oil on top if you like, and serve with the bread.

Fibre rating: MEDIUM

Per serving including bread: 3.9g fibre, 343 kcals, 14g fat, 4g saturated fat, 0.59g sodium

Watercress and fennel soup with indian spices

Many lettuces have no nutritional or fibre value. Watercress is one of the few exceptions. The potatoes are unpeeled to increase the fibre content and make the recipe easier.

Serves 2

2 tablespoons extra virgin olive or sunflower oil

1 medium onion, chopped

1 medium bulb fennel, chopped

2 small potatoes (100g/3½oz)

2 small garlic cloves, chopped

750ml (26fl oz) chicken stock or water

2 medium bunches watercress

To serve (optional)

2 heaped tablespoons low-fat plain bio yogurt

½ teaspoon garam masala (see page 98)

1 tablespoon chopped fennel fonds or dill

Heat the oil in a medium saucepan and gently cook the onion, fennel, potatoes and garlic covered with a lid for about 15 minutes until the vegetables are transparent and nearly cooked. Stir periodically to prevent them from burning. Add the stock or water, bring to the boil and simmer for about 10 minutes until the potatoes are soft.

Wash and roughly chop the watercress. Add to the pan of vegetables and cook for 5 minutes. Turn off the heat and liquidise until completely puréed for best results. Using a food processor will not purée the watercress completely.

Serve hot or at room temperature, but do not reheat for long or the vibrant colour will deteriorate.

Top the soup with a dollop of yogurt mixed with garam masala, if you wish, and chopped fennel fronds or dill.

Fibre rating: MEDIUM

Per serving not including serving suggestion: 4.8g fibre, 200 kcals, 13g fat, 2g saturated fat, 0.71g sodium

Chilled beetroot and dill soup

Beetroot is a cleansing vegetable and makes a comforting soup, which can be served either hot or cold. Any kind of stock can be used instead of chicken, including vegetable stock if you are looking for a vegetarian option. **Serves 4**

1 large red onion, finely chopped	850ml (1½ pints) light chicken stock
2 garlic cloves, chopped	1 heaped teaspoon cornflour (if serving the soup hot)
3 tablespoons olive oil	200g (7oz) low-fat plain set yogurt
700g (1½lb) beetroot, cooked in water, not in vinegar	1 heaped tablespoon chopped dill or mint
Salt and freshly ground black pepper	

Gently cook the onion and garlic in the olive oil until the onion is soft and transparent.

Peel the beetroot, cut the ends off and wash. Chop the beetroot into small pieces, add to the onion and cook gently for 5 minutes. Season with salt and pepper.

Add the chicken stock and bring to the boil. Simmer for about 10 minutes to infuse the flavour of the beetroot. Set aside.

Purée the soup in batches in a food processor or in a blender for finer results. Add a little more water if necessary, though this soup is best served thick. Taste and adjust the seasoning as required.

If serving the soup hot, stir the tablespoon of cornflour into 150g (5oz) of the yogurt. Add this yogurt to the last batch of soup being liquidised. Pour the soup back into the saucepan and cook gently for 2 minutes to reheat and cook the cornflour.

If serving the soup cold, make sure it has cooled before adding 150g (5oz) of the yogurt to the last batch of soup before liquidising.

Serve warm or chilled with a blob of yogurt and some chopped dill or mint on top.

Fibre rating: MEDIUM
Per serving: 4.2g fibre, 218 kcals, 10g fat, 2g saturated fat, 0.99g sodium

Tomato and tamarind soup
Tamarind is used in Asian cooking and can be found in Oriental shops and some supermarkets. It has a distinct sour flavour, which works well with sweet tomatoes. Tamarind paste, as opposed to whole tamarind, is the easiest way of using this spice. **Serves 4**

100g (3½oz) green Puy lentils	1 heaped tablespoon tamarind paste
4 tablespoons sunflower or olive oil	1 large chilli, finely chopped (optional)
2 garlic cloves	Salt and freshly ground black pepper
1 medium onion, finely chopped	**To serve (optional)**
2 teaspoons ground cumin seeds, toasted	Coarsely chopped coriander
1 teaspoon mustard seeds	Low-fat plain bio yogurt
800g (1¾ lb) tinned tomatoes	Naan or flat bread

First cook the lentils in a saucepan of water until tender. Do not add salt or they will take ages to cook, but season the water with a dash of oil and 1 of the garlic cloves to add flavour and help soften the lentil skins.

Heat the oil in another saucepan and gently cook the onion for about 10 minutes until soft. Add the remaining garlic, the cumin and mustard seeds and cook for a few more minutes.

Add the tomatoes to the spicy onion and cook for about 15 minutes, to reduce the liquid and intensify the flavour, making a sweet sauce.

Add the tamarind paste, cooked lentils and chilli, if using. Cook the mixture for about 5 minutes, then add about 500ml (18fl oz) water. Season with salt and pepper and cook for about 15 minutes to infuse the flavours. Add more water if need be, though this is a soup that should be quite thick.

Serve each bowl of soup topped with chopped coriander, a dollop of yogurt and accompanied by naan or flat bread for a 'meal in one'.

Fibre rating: MEDIUM
Per serving not including serving suggestion: 4.2g fibre, 230 kcals, 12g fat, 2g saturated fat, 0.29g sodium

Chicken broth with broccoli and cannellini beans

An Italian soup traditionally made with the new season's extra virgin olive oil. Omit the cannellini beans for a more authentic recipe, though they do provide extra fibre. **Serves 4**

- 4 heaped tablespoons cooked cannellini beans
- 4 thick slices country-style white bread
- 1 large garlic clove
- 1 litre (1¾ pints) homemade chicken stock
- Dash of sherry or vermouth
- Few slices dried wild mushrooms (optional)
- 400g (14oz) broccoli, or sprouting broccoli when in season
- Salt and freshly ground black pepper
- 25g (1oz) Parmesan cheese, grated
- Drizzle of good-quality, single-estate new season's extra virgin olive oil

If using tinned cannellini beans, rinse well with hot water and drain. Set aside.

Toast the bread and, while it is still hot, rub both sides with the cut side of the garlic. Cut in half and place two halves in each of four warmed shallow soup bowls. Add the cannellini beans and keep warm.

Pour the chicken stock into a pan, add the sherry or vermouth and the wild mushrooms, if using, and bring to the boil.

While the stock is heating, steam the broccoli for about 5 minutes. The broccoli should be cooked completely to bring out its flavour; only pasta is cooked al dente in Italy.

Place the broccoli on top of the beans and bread, season with salt and pepper, and pour over the hot stock. Sprinkle with the Parmesan, drizzle over the olive oil and serve immediately.

Fibre rating: HIGH
Per serving: 6.1g fibre, 207 kcals, 4g fat, 2g saturated fat, 0.77g sodium

Pea and tarragon soup

This soup may be served hot, at room temperature or chilled. Frozen peas are easier to deal with than fresh ones and make a greener-coloured soup. Serve with wholemeal bread or croûtons to increase the fibre. **Serves 4**

- 3 spring onions, or 1 small onion, finely chopped
- 2 tablespoons extra virgin olive oil
- 250g (9oz) potatoes, scrubbed well and cubed
- 1 large garlic clove, chopped
- Salt and freshly ground black pepper
- 400g (14oz) peas
- 850ml (1½ pints) chicken stock
- 4 tablespoons chopped tarragon
- 200g (7oz) low-fat plain bio yogurt

Cook the spring onions or onion in the olive oil in a saucepan for 5 minutes on a medium-high heat. Add the cubed potatoes and garlic, season with salt and pepper and cook for 10 minutes, stirring periodically to prevent them catching on the base of the pan.

If using fresh peas, add them to the pan and cook for a further 5 minutes. Add the chicken stock and simmer for 15 minutes. If using frozen peas, add after cooking the potatoes for 10 minutes and cook a further 5 minutes. Check that the potatoes are soft, add the tarragon and purée in a blender (not a food processor) for the best results.

Taste the soup and adjust the seasoning as necessary. If serving hot, top each bowlful with a dollop of yogurt. If serving chilled, add the yogurt to the soup once cooled and mix well. I like this soup best at room temperature.

Fibre rating: HIGH
Per serving: 6.1g fibre, 202 kcals, 7g fat, 1g saturated fat, 0.9g sodium

Grilled duck breast salad with endive and oranges

There is a beautiful variety of colours in this salad, particularly if you use a mixture of red and green endive. Warm Potato Salad (see page 67) makes a good accompaniment. **Serves 4 as starter or 2 as main dish**

2 large duck breasts, skinless if possible

2 small oranges (blood oranges when in season look great)

75g (3oz) blueberries or dried cherries

50g (2oz) roasted almonds or cashew nuts

4 small to medium endive (thick-stemmed variety)

4 tablespoons extra virgin olive oil

2 tablespoons chopped chives or chervil

Salt and freshly ground black pepper

Skin the duck breasts if necessary. Heat a griddle and cook the duck on a medium-high heat for about 10 minutes, turning halfway through. I prefer my duck pink in the middle; cook a few minutes more if you want it cooked through. Set aside to rest.

Top and tail the oranges and remove the skin and pith with a serrated knife, trimming down the sides. Cut the orange in half around the equator and slice. Place in a salad bowl along with the blueberries or cherries and nuts.

Cut the endive into large pieces, or leave the leaves whole. Add to the orange salad, mix well and add the olive oil, chives or chervil, and salt and pepper. Mix briefly and transfer the salad to serving plates, leaving the dressing in the bowl.

Slice the duck and add it to the dressing, mix briefly, then scatter it over the salad. Serve straight away.

Fibre rating: LOW
Per serving (starter): 2.7g fibre, 313 kcals, 23g fat, 4g saturated fat, 0.19g sodium

Tabbouleh

An easy salad that works well with plain grilled meat or fish or as part of a selection of mezze (Middle Eastern starters). Traditionally very little bulghur wheat is used, and plenty of fresh herbs. For a higher fibre content, use wholemeal bulghur wheat (found in good Middle Eastern shops). **Serves 4**

25g (1oz) bulghur wheat
125g (4½oz) flat-leaf parsley
100g (3½oz) mint
Juice of 1 large lemon
1 large tomato or 12 cherry
   tomatoes, finely diced

3 tablespoons extra virgin
   olive oil
Salt and freshly ground black
   pepper

Soak the bulghur wheat in just enough hot water to cover. Leave for 10 minutes and drain well, pressing out as much water as possible. Set aside.

Discard the stems of the herbs and rinse the leaves. Place on a tea-towel and leave to dry thoroughly – but be careful not to bruise the leaves or they will turn brown and discolour the salad.

Once the herbs are dry, chop coarsely and place in a bowl. Add the lemon juice, diced tomatoes, olive oil, bulghur wheat, salt and pepper. Mix well and serve. The tabbouleh will keep for several hours, during which time the flavours will develop further.

Fibre rating: LOW
Per serving: 2.2g fibre, 126 kcals, 9g fat, 1g saturated fat, 0.31g sodium

Courgette and cumin salad

Courgettes are another example of a low-fibre vegetable. For a higher fibre content, serve with warm pitta bread. This salad works well with simply grilled fish or chicken, or as part of a Middle Eastern mezze meal. **Serves 4**

500g (18oz) courgettes
Salt and freshly ground black
   pepper
1 tablespoon cumin seeds
1 large garlic clove, crushed
   with salt

200g (7oz) low-fat plain bio
   yogurt
1 tablespoon extra virgin olive
   oil (optional)
3 heaped tablespoons coarsely
   chopped mint

Coarsely grate the courgettes and mix with 1 tablespoon of salt. Leave in a colander to drain for 10 minutes. This releases excess water from the courgettes.

Lightly brown the cumin seeds in a dry frying pan and then grind in a spice grinder or using a pestle and mortar. Mix with the crushed garlic, yogurt, olive oil, if using, and salt and pepper.

Squeeze any remaining water from the courgettes with your hands – the salad should not be too wet. Mix the courgettes with the yogurt mixture and stir in the mint before serving.

Fibre rating: LOW
Per serving: 1.2g fibre, 77 kcals, 4g fat, 1g saturated fat, 0.23g sodium

Wild mushroom and bread salad

If fresh wild mushrooms are in season, omit dried mushrooms completely, using 500g (18oz) mushrooms in total. I have also used leftover foccacia for this recipe (see page 48) – remove the tomatoes and add to the salad before marinating. **Serves 4**

200g (7oz) decrusted Italian bread, e.g. ciabatta, focaccia
500g (18oz) mushrooms, such as field, shiitake or chestnut
2 tablespoons plus 75ml (3fl oz) extra virgin olive oil
2 large garlic cloves, finely chopped
1 heaped tablespoon chopped sage or rosemary
Salt and freshly ground black pepper
30g (generous 1oz) dried porcini mushrooms, soaked in just enough hot water to cover
3 tablespoons balsamic vinegar
Baby spinach or rocket leaves, to serve

Preheat the oven to 190°C/375°F/gas mark 5. Cut or tear the bread into 2.5cm (1in) cubes. Place the bread pieces on a baking tray and cook in the oven for about 15 minutes until golden brown and crisp on the outside.

Slice the mushrooms and cook in batches in a large frying pan with 1 tablespoon of the oil: add just enough mushrooms to cover the base of the pan each time and stir frequently, frying for about 1–2 minutes. When the mushrooms are nearly cooked, add half the garlic and half the sage or rosemary, season with salt and pepper, cook briefly, then spoon into a large bowl.

Drain the porcini and reserve the soaking liquid. Add 1 tablespoon of the oil to the frying pan and cook the porcini with the remaining garlic and sage or rosemary for a minute. Add the reserved soaking liquid and reduce back into the porcini. When the liquid has nearly disappeared, add the cooked fresh mushrooms back to the pan and mix briefly to coat in the tasty liquid. Spoon all the mushrooms back into the large bowl and add the cooked bread, balsamic vinegar, remaining 75ml (3fl oz) olive oil, salt and pepper. Mix well and leave to marinate for at least 30 minutes before serving.

Serve the salad on the spinach or rocket leaves.

Fibre rating: LOW
Per serving: 2.2g fibre, 461 kcals, 27g fat, 4g saturated fat, 0.53g sodium

Spinach, fennel and lentil salad

To make this lovely fresh-tasting salad more substantial, add 200g (7oz) bacon or 400g (14oz) cooked peeled prawns. Pan-fry them in a dash of olive oil and scatter over the lentils, with a squeeze of extra lemon juice. **Serves 4 as a starter or 2 as a main dish**

100g (3½oz) green or Puy lentils
1 garlic clove, unpeeled
5 tablespoons extra virgin olive oil
4 tablespoons lemon juice or red wine vinegar
Salt and freshly ground black pepper
125g (4½oz) baby spinach leaves, washed
250g (9oz) bulb fennel
2 tablespoons coarsely chopped basil, mint or parsley

Place the lentils in a saucepan of water with the whole unpeeled garlic clove. Bring to the boil and simmer for about 30 minutes until just soft. Drain well, remove the skin from the garlic and return the lentils to the saucepan, smashing the garlic and stirring it in to flavour them. Add 2 tablespoons of the olive oil and 2 tablespoons of the lemon juice or vinegar; season with salt and pepper.

Place the spinach leaves in a large mixing bowl. Remove any green fonds from the fennel, chop them and add to the lentils. Remove the triangular heart from the fennel and thinly slice the rest of the bulb. Add to the spinach leaves and add the remaining olive oil and lemon juice or vinegar; season with salt and pepper. Mix well and place on a large plate or individual plates.

Just before serving, mix the herbs with the lentils (if you add them too far in advance they may discolour.) Scatter the lentils over the spinach and fennel salad, and serve ideally while the lentils are warm.

Fibre rating: MEDIUM
Per serving (starter): 4.5g fibre, 217 kcals, 15g fat, 2g saturated fat, 0.15g sodium

Warm potato salad with green beans, spring onions and chives

For best results, choose good-quality waxy potatoes that don't break up when boiled. New potatoes, 'Charlotte', 'Ratte' and 'Rosvalt', are all good examples. Serve with grilled meats or fish. **Serves 4**

500g (18oz) waxy potatoes	2 heaped tablespoons chives
Salt and freshly ground black pepper	2 tablespoons extra virgin olive oil
200g (7oz) green beans	1 tablespoon good-quality wine vinegar
2 spring onions or 2 shallots	

Boil the potatoes whole in salted water until tender – this will take about 20–30 minutes, depending on their size. Keep them whole to keep the centres creamy. Steam the green beans until just cooked.

Finely chop the spring onions or shallots and chives and place in a salad bowl. Mix in the olive oil and vinegar.

When the potatoes are cooked, cut in half lengthways, add to the onion mixture, season with salt and pepper and mix well while still hot. Leave the potatoes to infuse in the flavours for 5 minutes, then add the green beans and serve the salad while still warm.

Fibre rating: MEDIUM
Per serving: 3.2g fibre, 146 kcals, 6g fat, 1g saturated fat, 0.5g sodium

Carrot, ginger and radicchio salad

Serve as part of a selection of salads or with boiled potatoes or warm wholemeal bread for added fibre. There is more fibre if the carrots are unpeeled so I suggest using organic varieties to avoid any chemical sprays on the skin. **Serves 4**

310g (11oz) carrots	4 tablespoons sesame oil
200g (7oz) radicchio	1 tablespoon rice vinegar
50g (2oz) pumpkin seeds	2 heaped teaspoons finely grated fresh ginger
Salt and freshly ground black pepper	

Peel and coarsely grate the carrots. Quarter the radicchio, remove the dense white heart and chop finely.

Mix the carrots and radicchio with the pumpkin seeds in a bowl and season with salt and pepper.

Make a dressing with the sesame oil, vinegar and ginger. Mix into the salad and serve straight away.

Fibre rating: MEDIUM
Per serving: 3.4g fibre, 174 kcals, 14g fat, 2g saturated fat, 0.22g sodium

Grilled peppers with raisins, red onions and pinenuts

Use red or yellow peppers or a combination of the two in this recipe; green peppers will not work as well. Serve with pitta bread or bruschetta (toast rubbed with garlic and extra virgin olive oil) for extra fibre. **Serves 4**

6 large red peppers
50g (2oz) pinenuts or slivered almonds
6 tablespoons extra virgin olive oil
1 medium to large red onion, quartered and thinly sliced
1 large garlic clove, crushed
50g (2oz) raisins (or sultanas)
3 tablespoons sherry vinegar or red wine vinegar
Salt and freshly ground black pepper

Grill the peppers whole until blackened all over, then place in a plastic bag to cool. Remove the skin and cut the peppers into strips, discarding the seeds. Scrape the peppers with a knife if the skins are particularly hard to remove. Do not rinse or you will wash away the flavour. Set aside.

While the peppers are grilling, cook the pinenuts or almonds in 1 tablespoon of the olive oil until light golden brown. Add the onion and garlic and cook slowly until soft. Add the raisins and mix briefly, then add the vinegar. Remove the mixture from the heat, season with salt and pepper, add the remaining oil and leave to soften the raisins for about 5 minutes.

To assemble the salad, place several thin strips of peppers on a plate. Scatter over some of the onion mixture and continue to layer the peppers and onions until all are used up.

Fibre rating: HIGH
Per serving: 5.2g fibre, 370 kcals, 26g fat, 3g saturated fat, 0.51g sodium

Wholemeal pitta bread and vegetable salad

Middle Eastern cuisine uses leftover pitta bread as the French use dry baguettes: here it soaks up all the lovely juices. Sumac has a sharpness similar to that of lemon zest and is available from Middle Eastern food stores. **Serves 4**

2 wholemeal pitta breads
1 large garlic clove, crushed with salt
Juice of 1 large lemon
100ml (3½fl oz) extra virgin olive oil
Salt and freshly ground black pepper
100g (3½oz) broccoli, cut into florets
100g (3½oz) green beans, halved
100g (3½oz) tomatoes, cut into large chunks
3 spring onions, finely chopped
½ cucumber (250g/9oz), peeled, halved and sliced
1 red pepper, deseeded and sliced
1 small Cos lettuce, coarsely chopped
4 heaped tablespoons coarsely chopped fresh coriander
1 tablespoon sumac (optional)

Preheat the oven to 200°C/400°F/gas mark 6. Heat the pitta bread in the oven for about 5–10 minutes, until crisp. Mix the crushed garlic, lemon juice, olive oil, salt and pepper in a large bowl. When the bread is cool enough to handle, break it into small pieces about 2cm (¾in) square and add to the bowl.

Steam or boil the broccoli and green beans until just cooked. Drain well.

Add the tomatoes, spring onions, cucumber, red pepper, lettuce and coriander to the bread mixture. Add the broccoli and green beans and mix well to coat. Leave to marinate for 10 minutes.

Taste the salad for seasoning and if necessary, add more salt and pepper. Serve as a starter, part of a selection of starters or as a healthy vegetarian main dish.

Fibre rating: HIGH
Per serving: 6.7g fibre, 466 kcals, 27g fat, 4g saturated fat, 0.6g sodium

Asparagus, bacon and chickpea salad
The poached eggs make this salad a meal in itself but can be omitted if you are looking for a lower fat content. Make sure the chickpeas are well rinsed, whether they are cooked from dried or tinned, to avoid flatulence. **Serves 2**

200g (7oz) cooked chickpeas
2 heaped tablespoons chopped flat-leaf parsley
1 heaped tablespoon chopped mint
2 tablespoons lemon juice or sherry vinegar
3 tablespoons extra virgin olive oil, plus extra for cooking

Salt and freshly ground black pepper
1 bunch asparagus (150g/5oz)
75g (3oz) smoked bacon lardons or cubes
1 large garlic clove
2 large handfuls rocket or other salad leaves
2 poached eggs (optional)

Rinse the chickpeas well, place in a bowl, and add the herbs with 1 tablespoon of the lemon juice or vinegar, 2 tablespoons of the oil, and salt and pepper. Mix well and set aside.

Boil or steam the asparagus for about 3–4 minutes, until just cooked. Drain and set aside.

Fry the bacon over medium-high heat in a dash of olive oil and add the garlic when the bacon is nearly golden and crispy. Set aside.

Place the rocket or other salad leaves in a bowl and add the asparagus and bacon. Pour in the remaining lemon juice or vinegar and the rest of the olive oil. Season with salt and pepper. Divide the salad leaves between two plates and serve with the chickpeas scattered over and a poached egg, if using, on top of each portion.

Fibre rating: HIGH
Per serving, including poached eggs: 5.8g fibre, 401 kcals, 25g fat, 6g saturated fat, 1.68g sodium

Celeriac remoulade
This is a French recipe traditionally using mayonnaise, though yogurt is a very good substitute, making it less rich. It is delicious served with smoked duck, chicken breasts or prosciutto ham and warm crusty bread. **Serves 4**

600g (1¼lb) celeriac, peeled and coarsely grated
3–4 heaped teaspoons French mustard

400g (14oz) low-fat plain bio yogurt
Salt and freshly ground black pepper

Place the celeriac in a large mixing bowl. Add the mustard and yogurt, season with salt and pepper and mix well to amalgamate. Leave to infuse for at least 15 minutes as this softens the celeriac. Serve as an accompaniment to smoked meats or charcuterie, along with warm crusty bread. It tastes even better the next day.

Fibre rating: HIGH
Per serving: 5.6g fibre, 91 kcals, 2g fat, 1g saturated fat, 0.67g sodium

3

Starters and Snacks

Asparagus and potato fritatta

As a lunch or snack option this is a yummy alternative to a sandwich. It is also good served with a salad on the side. Other vegetables can be substituted for the asparagus, such as green beans or spinach. **Serves 2 as a main dish or 4 as a light snack**

225g (8oz) unpeeled potatoes, cut into 3cm (1¼in) cubes
Salt and freshly ground black pepper
75g (3oz) asparagus (trimmed weight)
1 small leek, sliced
2 tablespoons extra virgin olive oil
4 eggs
50ml (2fl oz) milk
1 tablespoon coarsely chopped basil or parsley
1 tablespoon Parmesan cheese, grated
Salad, to serve (optional)

Boil the potatoes in salted water for about 10 minutes, until just soft. Cut off the tips of the asparagus and slice the stems in half at an angle. Add the asparagus to the potatoes when they are almost cooked and cook for a further 2 minutes. Drain well.

Meanwhile, gently cook the leek in the olive oil in a medium frying pan. When it is soft, add the potatoes and asparagus, season with salt and pepper and cook gently for a further 15 minutes, so that the potatoes and asparagus have time to absorb the flavour.

Break the eggs into a bowl and whisk gently with the milk, basil or parsley, salt and pepper.

Preheat the grill to high.

Pour the egg mixture over the vegetables and leave to cook gently for 5 minutes.

Scatter the Parmesan on the top and grill for 1–2 minutes until just set.

Leave to rest for 5 minutes before serving.

Fibre rating: LOW
Per serving (light snack): 1.2g fibre, 199 kcals, 13g fat, 3g saturated fat, 0.42g sodium

Marinated labnah balls

Labnah is a rich, thick yogurt which can be used in a variety of sweet or savoury dishes. Here it is rolled into small balls and then marinated in olive oil. Serve with warm wholemeal pitta bread and raw vegetables to increase the fibre content. **Makes about 16 balls**

500g (18oz) Greek-style thick live plain yogurt
1 teaspoon salt
2 tablespoons cumin seeds
2 tablespoons paprika
2 tablespoons thyme
1 large red chilli, halved or quartered
2 garlic cloves, halved
Sprigs of herbs (e.g. rosemary, thyme or oregano)
Extra virgin olive oil

Mix the yogurt with the salt, place in muslin or a washed dishcloth in a sieve over a bowl and leave to drain the whey for about 8 hours or overnight. (If in a hurry, 4 hours is just sufficient.) This thick yogurt cheese is then ready to be used in cooking savoury and sweet dishes.

To make the labnah balls, ensure the yogurt is properly drained for 8 hours and of a dense texture for best results. Roll the yogurt into 3cm (1¼in) balls, then roll in cumin seeds, paprika and thyme. Place in a bowl or sterilised jam jar, and add the red chilli, garlic and sprigs of herbs, and cover with olive oil to marinate.

They keep for a couple of weeks in the fridge and are perfect to eat when your cupboard looks bare: serve them on toast, smeared on grilled meats, or in sandwiches as a healthy alternative to mayonnaise or cream cheese.

Fibre rating: LOW
Per serving (2 labnah balls): 0g fibre, 86 kcals, 8g fat, 3g saturated fat, 0.29g sodium

Baked endive wrapped in prosciutto

Endive is sometimes known as chicory. This is a simple dish to serve on its own with some bread to mop up the juices. It's also good with baked white fish or a grilled lamb or pork chop.

Serves 4

4 large heads endive bulbs
8 large basil leaves
100g (3½oz) prosciutto or speck, thinly sliced
1 large garlic clove, finely chopped
25g (1oz) wholemeal or white breadcrumbs
25g (1oz) Parmesan cheese, grated
1 tablespoon extra virgin olive oil
Freshly ground black pepper
250ml (9fl oz) chicken stock

Preheat the oven to 190°C/375°F/gas mark 5.

Cut the endive in half lengthways. Place a basil leaf on each half and wrap a slice of prociutto round the endive. Place in a gratin dish about 20cm x 26cm (8 x 10in) so that they fit snugly in one layer.

Mix the garlic with the breadcrumbs, Parmesan, olive oil and pepper. (The oil helps to crisp the breadcrumbs, making a crunchy topping). Scatter over the endive.

Pour the stock carefully into the dish down one side – avoid soaking the breadcrumbs. It should come about halfway up the endive. Cover with foil and bake for 45 minutes. Remove the foil and cook a further 30 minutes, until the endive is soft at the thickest end.

Take the dish out of the oven and leave to rest for at least 15 minutes before serving.

Fibre rating: LOW
Per serving, with wholemeal breadcrumbs: 2.8g fibre, 141 kcals, 8g fat, 3g saturated fat, 0.87g sodium

Stuffed vine leaves

A combination of red rice and pearl barley is used to increase the fibre content of this dish. Vine leaves are often used in Mediterranean countries, where they grow in abundance. If using fresh vine leaves, blanch in salted water for 2 minutes and drain before stuffing. **Serves 6**

50g (2oz) pinenuts

3 tablespoons extra virgin olive oil

1 large onion, finely chopped

2 garlic cloves, finely chopped

150g (5oz) mixture of red rice and pearl barley

50g (2oz) currants

1 teaspoon ground allspice

Salt and freshly ground black pepper

4 tablespoons chopped mint

250g (9oz) packet vine leaves in salt water

250g (9oz) fennel bulb, cut into thin wedges or slices

Low-fat plain bio yogurt, to serve (optional)

Gently cook the pinenuts in 2 tablespoons of the oil, then add the onion and garlic and cook for about 10 minutes until the onion is soft and the pinenuts golden. Add the rice and barley, currants and allspice, season with salt and pepper and mix briefly.

Pour over 600ml (1 pint) hot water, cover with a lid and cook for 40 minutes. Remove the lid and, if there is still some water left, reduce until the mixture is dry. Spoon into a bowl and add the chopped mint.

Remove the vine leaves from the packet, cover with boiling water and leave to soak for 5 minutes. Drain well.

Pour the remaining oil into an ovenproof dish or thick-based saucepan, about 23cm (9in) wide. Scatter over the fennel pieces so that they cover the base.

Preheat the oven, if using, to 180°C/350°F/gas mark 4.

Place a vine leaf on a work surface, with the rough side facing up. Place 1 level tablespoon of the rice filling in the middle of the leaf (depending on the size), fold over from the bottom, folding the sides into the middle as you go, and roll up tightly to keep it sealed. Place on top of the fennel, folded side down. Repeat until all the filling is used and fit the stuffed leaves snugly into the dish or pan in one layer so that they don't open up when cooking. If your dish or pan is not wide enough for one layer, arrange another layer on top, drizzling a little olive oil between the layers.

Pour in enough water to come three-quarters of the way up the vine leaves. Cover with a lid or foil and place in the oven for 1 hour, or simmer very gently on the stove for 45 minutes. When cooking on the stove the water might evaporate, but that is ok – just add a dash more if not cooked through.

Remove from the heat and leave uncovered to cool. Serve warm or at room temperature with a dollop of yogurt.

Fibre rating: MEDIUM
Per serving, not including yogurt: 3.8g fibre, 200 kcals, 12g fat, 1g saturated fat, 1.13g sodium

Dukkah (egyptian nut dip) *Eat with high-fibre flatbread if you want to make this into a high-fibre recipe; dunking it in extra virgin olive oil will make the dukkah stick to it. Delicious with thick-set yogurt or labnah and raw vegetables such as radishes, spring onions and tomatoes.* **Serves 6**

240g (8½oz) cooked chickpeas, rinsed and drained
100g (3½oz) blanched hazelnuts
100g (3½oz) sesame seeds
2 heaped tablespoons coriander seeds
1 tablespoon cumin seeds
1 heaped teaspoon sea salt
1 heaped teaspoon freshly ground black pepper

Preheat the oven to 180°C/350°F/gas mark 4. Place the chickpeas on a roasting tray in the oven and cook for about 45 minutes until dry and slightly crunchy. Meanwhile, cook the hazelnuts and sesame seeds on separate trays in the oven for about 15 minutes, until both are golden brown. Set aside and leave to cool.

Dry-roast the coriander and then the cumin seeds in a frying pan on a medium heat for a few minutes until they start to colour very slightly and give off a mild aroma. Watch them carefully as they can burn very easily.

Grind the spices first, using a pestle and mortar for best results. (A solid bowl and the end of a rolling pin make a good substitute.) Place the spices in a bowl. It might be easier to grind in batches. Then grind half the sesame seeds and add the rest whole to the spices. Coarsely grind the hazelnuts and finally the chickpeas, so they keep some texture.

Mix the ground ingredients together and add the salt and pepper. Taste to check for correct seasoning and adjust as necessary.

Serve the dukkah as suggested above. It will keep for several weeks in an airtight container.

Fibre rating: MEDIUM
Per serving: 4g fibre, 254 kcals, 22g fat, 2g saturated fat, 0.61g sodium

Bruschetta with chard, borlotti beans and anchovy sauce *A great Italian recipe, ideal for non-meat eaters. Some chard has large white stalks, but these can be used as well in the recipe: boil for longer and cut into small pieces. Substitute sprouting broccoli if you prefer.* **Serves 4**

400g (14oz) chard leaves
400g (14oz) tin borlotti or cannellini beans, drained and rinsed
4 large slices sourdough bread
Salt and freshly ground black pepper
1 garlic clove

For the anchovy sauce
50g (2oz) tin anchovies in oil, drained, or jar of salted anchovies, rinsed and drained
1 tablespoon chopped rosemary
2 tablespoons lemon juice
50ml (2fl oz) extra virgin olive oil
Freshly ground black pepper

To make the anchovy sauce, put the anchovies and rosemary in a food processor with the lemon juice. Mix together and slowly add the olive oil. (You can also make the sauce by hand using a pestle and mortar.) Taste to see if you need to add more oil or lemon juice, if you prefer a milder anchovy flavour. Season with pepper and set aside. If the sauce separates, just give it a good stir before serving – it is not meant to be a mayonnaise.

Cook the chard in boiling water until tender. Drain and set aside. Place the chard and beans in separate bowls and add ½ tablespoon of the anchovy sauce to each. Mix and season with salt and pepper.

Toast the bread and, while it is still hot, rub on both sides with the cut side of the garlic. Place the bruschetta on plates, place the chard on top, scatter over the beans and finally drizzle over the remaining anchovy sauce. Serve straight away.

Fibre rating: MEDIUM
Per serving: 4.3g fibre, 331 kcals, 15g fat, 2g saturated fat, 1.15g sodium

Shrimps on toast

For best results try to find the tiny shrimps which the French call 'grey shrimps' or which the English use in potted shrimp recipes. You could serve these as nibbles at a party using bite-sized pieces of toast. **Serves 2 as a starter or light snack**

100g (3½oz) cooked shrimps
100g (3½oz) cooked green
   beans, diced
2 tablespoons coarsely
   chopped flat-leaf parsley
½ grilled or raw red pepper or
   ½ large mild red chilli,
   deseeded and diced
Juice of ½ lemon

3 tablespoons extra virgin
   olive oil
Freshly ground black pepper
2 slices wholemeal bread
1 garlic clove
Salad leaves, such as rocket
   (optional)

Rinse the shrimps and dry well on kitchen paper. Mix the shrimps with the diced beans, chopped parsley, diced chilli or pepper, lemon juice, 1 tablespoon of the extra virgin olive oil, and pepper. Leave to marinate for a few minutes.

Toast the bread and, while it is still warm, rub with the cut side of the garlic. Place the toasts on plates on top of some salad leaves, if using, and spoon over the shrimp mixture.

Finally drizzle over the remaining oil and serve straight away.

Fibre rating: MEDIUM
Per serving: 3.8g fibre, 300 kcals, 18g fat, 3g saturated fat, 0.7g sodium

Potato galette with wholemeal pastry

A galette is an open pastry tart. This simple yet sophisticated dish needs just a green salad to accompany it. As with all pastry dishes, this is a relatively high-fat recipe, so is best avoided if you are on a low-fat diet. **Serves 4 as main, 6 as starter**

400g (14oz) ready-made wholemeal pastry
250g (9oz) baking potatoes, unpeeled
250g (9oz) sweet potatoes, unpeeled
Salt and freshly ground black pepper
2 tablespoons chopped sage

4 tablespoons extra virgin olive oil
1 garlic clove, smashed with salt into a pulp
3 heaped teaspoons mushroom and truffle paste
1 egg yolk, mixed with 1 tablespoon milk for the egg wash

On a floured work surface, roll out the pastry into a rough square about 35cm (14in) across and 3mm (⅛in) thick. Move the pastry round by a quarter turn with each roll to prevent it from sticking to the work surface and to create a uniform shape. Place a sheet of foil on a board or large plate, place the pastry on it and chill for 15 minutes.

Place a baking tray in the oven and preheat to 200°C/400°F/gas mark 6. Thinly slice the potatoes and sweet potatoes. Place the slices in a bowl and season with salt and pepper. Mix in the sage, oil, crushed garlic and truffle paste.

Remove the pastry from the fridge and trim into a 33cm (13in) circle. Arrange the potato mixture in the middle, leaving a 5cm (2in) border around the edges. Fold up the sides of the pastry in about five turns, encasing the potatoes but leaving the centre showing.

Glaze the pastry edges with egg wash and lift the pastry, still on the foil, onto the warmed baking tray. Bake for 30 minutes until the pastry is light golden brown. Turn the heat down to 180°C/350°F/gas mark 4 and cover the potato centre with a little sheet of foil. Cook for a further 30 minutes, then remove from the oven, leave to rest for at least 15 minutes, and serve.

Fibre rating: HIGH
Per serving (starter): 6.7g fibre, 517 kcals, 31g fat, 8g saturated fat, 0.61g sodium

Avocado, fennel and cucumber relish with flatbread

This relish works well served with a selection of other salads. The high fibre content of this recipe comes from the wholemeal pitta bread, so use white pitta bread if you need to decrease the fibre. **Serves 4**

½ large cucumber
1 teaspoon sea salt
1 teaspoon fennel seeds, ground or 200g (7oz) bulb fennel
1 ripe avocado
1 tablespoon tahini or toasted sesame seeds
1 garlic clove, crushed with salt

2 tablespoons coarsely chopped tarragon
3 heaped tablespoons low-fat plain bio yogurt
Freshly ground black pepper
1 tablespoon lemon juice (optional)
4 large wholemeal pitta or flatbread, to serve

Peel the cucumber and slice in half lengthways. Remove the seeds with a teaspoon, slice into thin strips and chop finely. Place the cucumber pieces in a colander and mix with the salt. Leave to degorge for 15 minutes. This releases some of the liquid from the cucumber, making the relish less watery. Squeeze the cucumber between your hands to release the remaining juices and place in a bowl.

Add the ground fennel to the cucumber. If using fresh fennel, trim any green fronds and chop them finely. Cut out and discard the tough heart and chop the rest into small pieces. Add to the cucumber along with the chopped fronds. Peel, stone and coarsely chop the avocado and add to the bowl. You could use a food processor to do the chopping if preferred.

Stir the tahini paste well, as it tends to separate if left to stand, then add it or the sesame seeds to the bowl. Add the crushed garlic, tarragon and yogurt, season with pepper and mix well. **Taste** and add more salt if needed – though enough may have already been added with the garlic and cucumber. Add the lemon juice if the yogurt used is not very tart.

Fibre rating: HIGH
Per serving including bread: 7.3g fibre, 403 kcals, 14g fat, 2g saturated fat, 0.95g sodium

4

Fish

Sardine kofta with tomatoes and spices

This is a dish from Morocco where really fresh sardines are plentiful. You could try substituting any oily fish such as mackerel or grey mullet; the freshness of the fish is more important than the type. Serve with warm pitta bread and salad. **Serves 4**

450g (1lb) fresh sardine fillets
1 heaped teaspoon cumin seeds
1 heaped teaspoon coriander seeds
½ large chilli, chopped (optional)
2 garlic cloves, chopped
2 tablespoons fresh breadcrumbs, wholemeal or plain
2 heaped tablespoons coarsely chopped fresh coriander
Salt and freshly ground black pepper
2 tablespoons extra virgin olive oil
400g (14oz) tin chopped tomatoes
1 small lemon, cut into thin slices

Remove any large bones remaining in the sardine fillets and rinse to clean away any scales or blood. Don't worry about small bones down the middle of the fish. Drain on kitchen paper. Grind the cumin and coriander seeds in a spice grinder or pestle and mortar. Place the fish in a food processor with the ground cumin and coriander, the chilli, if using, garlic, breadcrumbs and half the fresh coriander. Season well with salt and pepper and mix thoroughly.

Preheat the oven to 150°C/300°F/gas mark 2. Roll the sardine mixture into about 20 x 25g (1oz) balls. Set aside.

Heat the olive oil in a large ovenproof sauté pan (or tagine, if you have one), then add the tomatoes and cook until reduced, stirring periodically to prevent them burning on the base of the pan. Add the sardine balls and cook on a medium-high heat for 1 minute. Turn the balls over; add 2 tablespoons water so that the tomatoes are not too dry. Lay the lemon slices on top of the balls; cover the pan with a lid and place in the oven for 10 minutes.

Remove the sardine kofta from the oven and scatter with the remaining fresh coriander. Serve hot or at room temperature.

Fibre rating: LOW
Per serving: 1g fibre, 276 kcals, 16g fat, 4g saturated fat, 0.72g sodium

Grilled trout with almonds

It is always good to revisit old classics and make them healthy. Serve with a watercress and green bean salad and boiled new potatoes for added fibre. The fish can also be griddled or baked (see picture on page 82). **Serves 2**

Drizzle of olive oil, for greasing
4 tablespoons extra virgin olive oil
2 tablespoons lemon juice or white wine vinegar
2 heaped tablespoons coarsely chopped flat-leaf parsley
1 heaped tablespoon capers, rinsed and finely chopped
25g (1oz) almonds, roasted in a medium oven for about 10 minutes, then finely chopped
Salt and freshly ground black pepper
2 x 200g (7oz) whole trout, cleaned and gutted

Preheat the grill to high. Cover the grill tray with foil and drizzle over a little oil so the fish doesn't stick when cooking. Mix the olive oil with the lemon juice or vinegar, parsley, capers and almonds. Season with salt and pepper, and set aside. This can be prepared in advance.

Cook the fish for about 4 minutes on each side. Reduce the heat or lower the shelf if the skin is starting to burn before the fish is cooked. Check that it is ready by lifting a little of the flesh by the middle fin. If the flesh is just cooked through to the bone, turn the trout over to hide the incision and serve straight away with the almond salsa.

If baking the fish, preheat the oven to 200°C/400°F/gas mark 6, and cook for about 10–15 minutes until the eye is opaque and the flesh just firm.

Fibre rating: LOW
Per serving: 1.4g fibre, 503 kcals, 37g fat, 4g saturated fat, 0.21g sodium

Mussel, saffron and yogurt stew

I wanted to include a shellfish recipe and this is an interesting way to cook mussels. The recipe is low in fibre but if you served some lentils or a chickpea salad with it the fibre would be increased.

Serves 6

2kg (4½lb) mussels

100g (3½oz) brown or white rice

2 large pinches of saffron strands

50ml (2fl oz) dry white vermouth or sherry

100ml (3½fl oz) white wine

1 large red onion, finely chopped

1 large carrot, finely chopped

2 large garlic cloves

3 tablespoons extra virgin olive oil

200g (7fl oz) Greek-style yogurt, or low-fat plain yogurt mixed with 1 heaped teaspoon cornflour

1 small bunch coriander or dill, coarsely chopped

Make sure the mussels are debearded and properly cleaned. Wash them in several changes of water and drain.

Cook the rice in boiling water to cover with a pinch of saffron for about 10 minutes, or longer for brown rice, until the water has evaporated and the rice is just tender. Set aside to steam, covered with a lid. Soak the remaining saffron in the vermouth or sherry.

Heat a large saucepan with a tight-fitting lid. Unless you have a very big pan, cook the mussels in batches, making sure they cover the base of the pan – don't put in too many at once or they won't cook evenly. Throw the mussels in with some of the wine, cover and cook for about 2 minutes. Lift the lid after 1 minute and check that the mussels are cooking quickly and starting to open. Stir well, cover again and cook for another 1–2 minutes, depending on their size. Cook just until the shells open – discard any that fail to open. Pour into a colander that is resting inside a bowl to collect the juices. Rinse the pan briefly and repeat until all mussels are cooked. Remove the shells once cool, discarding the shells. Pour the cooking juices into a container, discarding the sediment, and set aside.

Rinse the pan again before cooking the base of the stew. Gently cook the onion, carrot and garlic in the olive oil for 10 minutes until they are soft and the onion is transparent. Add the saffron and vermouth and bring to the boil. Reduce for a minute or two. Add the reserved cooking liquid and the yogurt mixed with cornflour (the latter prevents it separating). Bring to a simmer, then add the mussels and half the chopped herb. Remove from the heat.

Divide the rice between six warmed bowls and pour the stew on top. Sprinkle with the remaining herb and serve straight away

Fibre rating: LOW
Per serving with brown rice: 1.3g fibre, 251 kcals, 12g fat, 3g saturated fat, 0.37g sodium

Monkfish kebabs marinated with herbs and yogurt

The yogurt helps to tenderise the fish. Salmon or cod can be used instead of monkfish if you like. Serve with brown rice, or lentils and braised spinach, to increase the fibre content. **Serves 4**

600g (1¼lb) monkfish fillet, cut into 2.5cm (1in) cubes

200g (7oz) set low-fat plain yogurt

2 tablespoons chervil or dill, coarsely chopped

Salt and freshly ground black pepper

Skewers

Mix the monkfish cubes in a bowl with the yogurt and half the chervil. Season with salt and pepper and leave to marinate. Preheat the grill to high.

Place the monkfish pieces on skewers or line them in rows on a baking sheet, smearing over any excess yogurt from the bowl.

Cook for about 5–10 minutes, depending on the size of the cubes of fish and the heat of the grill. They should be just firm to the touch.

Serve the kebabs on a bed of rice or salad if you like, pour over the cooking juices and scatter over the remaining chervil or dill for a fresh taste.

Fibre rating: LOW

Per serving: 0g fibre, 157 kcals, 6g fat, 3g saturated fat, 0.35g sodium

Syrian stuffed fish with rice and tamarind

Any round fish that is fresh will work in this recipe. The tartness of tamarind combines well with the sweetness of the figs. Serve with spinach or green beans for added fibre.

Serves 6

1.5kg (3lb 5oz) sea bass, bream or other round fish large enough to stuff

2 tablespoons extra virgin olive oil, plus extra for greasing

50g (2oz) pinenuts

50g (2oz) almonds, coarsely chopped

1 medium red onion, finely chopped

2 garlic cloves, chopped

100g (3½oz) dried figs, chopped

175g (6oz) brown or white basmati rice

Salt and freshly ground black pepper

Small pinch of saffron, soaked in 1 tablespoon water

Grated zest and juice of large lime

2 heaped teaspoons grated fresh ginger

2 tablespoons tamarind paste

2 tablespoons brown sugar

Chopped coriander, to serve

Ask the fishmonger to scale, gut and clean the fish. Rinse the fish just before cooking to remove any remaining blood. Set aside on kitchen paper to drain.

Pour the olive oil into a large pan, add the pinenuts and almonds and cook briefly until they turn a light golden brown. Add the onion and garlic, turn the heat down to low and continue cooking for a further 10 minutes until the onion is soft. Add the figs, rice and some salt, stir briefly, then add the saffron and enough water just to cover the rice if using white rice, a little more if using brown. Bring to the boil and simmer for about 10 minutes for white rice and 30 minutes for brown. Leave covered for 10 minutes off the heat. The rice should be just cooked. Remove the lid and, if there is any water left, evaporate until dry. Stir in the lime zest. Leave to cool completely unless cooking the fish immediately.

Preheat the oven with a baking tray to 200°C/400°F/gas mark 6.

In a small saucepan, heat the lime juice, ginger, tamarind, sugar and about 2 tablespoons water. Stir and simmer briefly until the sugar has dissolved. Set aside.

Prepare a piece of foil big enough to seal the fish in and drizzle a little olive oil in the middle so the fish doesn't stick. Place the fish on the foil and place half the tamarind sauce in the belly. Stuff as much of the rice as possible into the fish, placing the rest next to it as it will be all sealed in the foil. Pour the remaining tamarind sauce on top of the fish. Season with salt and pepper. Fold up the sides of the foil, sealing all the edges well. Remove the heated baking tray from the oven and carefully place the fish on it. Cook the fish in the oven for about 20 minutes. If you have prepared the rice in advance and it is cold, allow a further 10 minutes. The fish is cooked when the eye looks opaque or the colour of poached eggs.

To serve, place the fish on an oval plate – it should slide easily off the foil if well greased. Sprinkle over some coriander for colour.

Fibre rating: LOW
Per serving with brown rice: 2.8g fibre, 591 kcals, 25g fat, 5g saturated fat, 0.51g sodium

Mackerel simmered in miso soup

This Japanese dish uses miso to give a delicious nutty, salty flavour. Dashi is a fish stock made with bonito (dried tuna) flakes. Try using other oily fish if good fresh mackerel are not available. Serve with steamed mangetout and wholemeal or plain rice. **Serves 4**

4 mackerel fillets, about 400g (14oz) total weight
3g packet bonito flakes (packet miso soup or fish stock can be substituted)
2 tablespoons sake
2 tablespoons mirin or dry white vermouth

1 teaspoon sugar
1 small piece fresh ginger, peeled and cut into 16 very thin slivers
1 heaped tablespoon miso paste
2 thin spring onions, thinly sliced

Wash and clean the mackerel fillets and dry on kitchen paper.
Make the dashi (fish stock) by placing the bonito flakes in a measuring jug and pouring 200ml (7fl oz) boiling water over them. Leave for 5 minutes and drain, discarding the bonito flakes. (A thrifty Japanese would reuse the bonito flakes, mixing them with plain rice and sesame seeds or with wilted spinach). Mix in the sake, mirin or vermouth and sugar.
Warm a serving dish. Place 4 thin slivers of ginger on top of each mackerel fillet. Pour the dashi into a large sauté or frying pan and add the mackerel fillets. Bring the liquid just to the boil, cover with a lid and cook the fish for 3–4 minutes, depending on size, until it is just firm and cooked.
Remove the mackerel fillets from the pan, place on the warmed serving dish and keep warm. Add the miso to the cooking liquid and bring to the boil. Simmer for a couple of minutes to reduce a little. Add the sliced spring onions and pour the sauce over the mackerel. Serve straight away with rice and mangetout.

Fibre rating: LOW
Per serving: 0.1g fibre, 251 kcals, 16g fat, 3g saturated fat, 0.17g sodium

Baked fish parcels with julienne of vegetables
An attractive dinner party recipe. I suggest you use thin pieces of fish rather than thick as the bright colour of the vegetables will diminish if cooked for too long. Serve with lentils, potatoes with skins or borlotti beans to increase the fibre. **Serves 4**

150g (5oz) leeks, thinly sliced
3 tablespoons sunflower oil
1 large garlic clove, grated
1 heaped teaspoon grated fresh ginger
150g (5oz) carrots, coarsely grated

150g (5oz) mangetout, thinly sliced
2 tablespoons chopped tarragon
4 x 100g (3½oz) fillets of white fish, e.g. cod, bream, monkfish
4 tablespoons dry white vermouth or white wine

Place a large baking tray in the oven and preheat to 200°C/400°F/gas mark 6.
Cook the leeks in 1 tablespoon of the sunflower oil on medium-high heat for 2 minutes. Stir frequently to prevent browning. Once softened, add the ginger and garlic and cook for a further minute. Remove from the heat and stir in the carrots, mangetout and tarragon. Season if liked and set aside.
Cut 4 large sheets of foil about 40cm (15½in) square. Drizzle ½ tablespoon of oil three-quarters of the way up each piece of foil (so that when folded, this becomes the middle of the parcel). Divide the vegetables evenly between the foil squares, placing them on the oil. Top with a fillet of fish and season with salt and pepper. Pour 1 tablespoon vermouth over each fillet and fold up the foil. Seal by carefully folding over both sides several times and pressing down well. Finally fold over the top several times so that the fish is completely sealed.
Place the fish parcels on the preheated baking tray, overlapping the ends of the parcels if necessary. Cook in the oven for 10–15 minutes, depending on the thickness of the fish. To check that the fish is cooked, carefully unfold one, taking care not to let the steam burn you.
Transfer the fish parcels to serving plates and let your guests open them up themselves. Bear in mind that they will carry on cooking if not opened immediately.

Fibre rating: LOW
Per serving: 2.6g fibre, 200 kcals, 9g fat, 1g saturated fat, 0.37g sodium

Thai prawn balls in lemon grass fish broth

Any firm white fish can be substituted for the prawns if you prefer. Choose noodles and vegetables with appropriate fibre levels to serve with. Mangetout and sugar snap peas work particularly well with this dish. **Serves 4**

350g (12oz) unpeeled raw prawns (275g/10oz peeled weight)

14 kaffir lime leaves

2 lemon grass sticks, cut into chunks

2 heaped tablespoons coarsely chopped Thai basil or coriander

2 tablespoons Thai fish sauce

2 teaspoons cornflour

2 egg whites

50g (2oz) green beans, finely chopped into discs

1 tablespoon coarsely chopped galangal (optional)

Few coriander sprigs, to garnish

Peel the prawns, placing the prawn shells in a pan. Cover with 1 litre (1¾ pints) water, 4 of the lime leaves and 1 of the lemon grass sticks. Bring to the boil and simmer for 30 minutes. Drain into a measuring jug to make sure you have about 500ml (18fl oz) tasty prawn broth. Rinse the pan and place the prawn stock back in the pan, discarding any sediment at the bottom. Set aside.

De-vein the prawns, removing the thin black food sac down the middle, rinse and drain well on kitchen paper. Remove the central vein from 6 of the lime leaves and discard; chop the leaves. Place the prawns and lime leaves in a food processor and add the basil or coriander, fish sauce, cornflour and egg whites. Blend well, stir in the green beans and set aside to rest. Test whether the mixture has enough seasoning by cooking a little ball of it in some of the stock. Then, using your hands, form the mixture into 20 balls.

Bring the prawn stock back to the boil, add the remaining lime leaves, the remaining lemon grass and the galangal, if using. Bring to the boil again and simmer for a few minutes. Remove the lemon grass and lime leaves with a slotted spoon.

Add the prawn balls to the stock, cooking as many as you can at one time. Cook for 4 minutes, turning over halfway through.

Warm four bowls and divide the fish balls between them. Pour the broth over and scatter a few sprigs of coriander on top. Serve straight away.

Fibre rating: LOW

Per serving: 0g fibre, 81 kcals, 1g fat, 0g saturated fat, 0.76g sodium

Grilled swordfish with cannellini bean salad

Any fish can be used in this recipe, just as long as it is fresh. Other beans can be used in the salad if necessary. Basil mayonnaise is a delicious accompaniment if you don't mind the fat content. **Serves** 4

4 x 100g (3½oz) swordfish steaks

2 heaped tablespoons finely chopped basil

2 tablespoons extra virgin olive oil, plus extra for the fish

Salt and freshly ground black pepper

4 lemon wedges

For the bean salad

2 tablespoons extra virgin olive oil

175g (6oz) bulb fennel, thinly sliced

2 red peppers, deseeded and thinly sliced

1 large garlic clove, chopped

Salt and freshly ground black pepper

400g (14oz) tin cannellini beans, drained and rinsed

150g (5oz) baby spinach, washed

To make the salad, heat the oil in a pan and add the fennel, red peppers, garlic and salt and pepper. Cook over a medium heat, covered with a lid, for about 20 minutes, stirring periodically until the vegetables are soft.

Add the beans and cook for a further minute. Add the spinach, stirring until it just wilts. This can be served either hot or cold.

To cook the fish, heat a griddle until hot. Finely chop the basil, mix with the oil and season with salt and pepper. Set aside. Lightly oil the fish and cook for about 2–3 minutes, depending on its thickness. Season with salt and pepper.

Serve the bean salad with the fish on top. Drizzle over the basil oil and serve with a wedge of lemon to squeeze over the fish.

Fibre rating: MEDIUM

Per serving: 3.1g fibre, 249 kcals, 16g fat, 3g saturated fat, 0.39g sodium

Baked salmon with lentils and spinach

If you haven't tried lentils with salmon before you may be surprised at how well they complement one another. Lentils are a good source of fibre and can be easily prepared in advance. **Serves** 4

150g (5oz) green or Puy lentils

1 large garlic clove, quartered

2 tablespoons extra virgin olive oil, plus extra for the fish

100g (3½oz) spinach, coarsely chopped

Salt and freshly ground black pepper

4 x 150g (5oz) salmon fillets

150g (5oz) low-fat Greek style yogurt

To serve

4 medium tomatoes, halved and roasted, or 2 large grilled and skinned red peppers, cut into strips

Place the lentils in a saucepan and cover generously with water. Add the garlic and 1 tablespoon of the oil and bring to the boil. Reduce the heat and simmer for 30 minutes, until the lentils are just soft. Drain well, remove the skin from the garlic and set aside.

Rinse the saucepan to remove any lentil sediment on the sides. Add the remaining oil to the pan along with the spinach leaves. Cook the spinach gently for a few minutes until it just wilts. Add the drained cooked lentils and garlic and season with salt and pepper, mixing well. Set aside.

Heat a griddle or grill and very lightly smear the fish with a little oil. Season with salt and pepper and cook for about 5–7 minutes on each side, depending on the thickness, until just cooked. Salmon is one fish that can be served slightly rare.

Rewarm the lentils and stir in the yogurt. Remove immediately from the heat and serve straight away. The yogurt will separate if overheated.

Place the lentils on warmed plates and serve the salmon on top with roasted tomatoes or grilled peppers to add extra sweetness.

Fibre rating: MEDIUM

Per serving: 4.3g fibre, 487 kcals, 25g fat, 4g saturated fat, 0.63g sodium

Salmon wrapped in vine leaves with couscous

If only little tins of very fiery harissa are available, mix with 1 large grilled red pepper, finely chopped, and ½ teaspoon each ground cumin and coriander seeds. Increase the fibre content if needed with some high-fibre vegetables. **Serves 4**

16 vine leaves (100g/3½oz) in salted water (can be omitted if unavailable)

4 x 150g (5oz) salmon fillets (cod can be substituted)

Salt and freshly ground black pepper

1 small bunch thyme

Drizzle of olive oil

For the couscous

150g (5oz) bulb fennel, finely chopped and fronds (if any) reserved

150g (5oz) green beans, finely chopped

2 garlic cloves, chopped

2 tablespoons extra virgin olive oil

Salt and freshly ground black pepper

25g (1oz) currants

1 teaspoon fennel seeds, ground

½ teaspoon ground cinnamon

100g (3½oz) couscous

2 tablespoons coarsely chopped flat-leaf parsley

1 tablespoon coarsely chopped mint

2 heaped tablespoons good-quality harissa sauce

1 lemon, cut into wedges

Pour boiling water over the salted vine leaves and leave for 5 minutes before rinsing well and squeezing to remove excess water.

Spread a vine leaf out on a board and place a salmon fillet on top. Season with salt and pepper and put a couple of thyme sprigs on top of the fish. Fold over the leaf and place another leaf on top, wrapping it underneath. Place two more leaves on top and wrap underneath. Lightly grease with olive oil on both sides. Make three more parcels in the same way.

Heat a griddle to medium high or preheat the oven to 200°C/400°F/gas mark 6. Cook the fish parcels on both sides for 6–12 minutes depending on the thickness and heat of the griddle, or bake in the oven for 10–15 minutes. Press lightly to make sure the fish is firm. Leave to rest for a few minutes before serving; the fish can be served hot or cold.

Meanwhile, make the couscous: cook the fennel, beans and garlic in the olive oil for about 20 minutes in a covered pan. Season with salt and pepper, stirring periodically and dropping any condensation from the lid inside to make the vegetables cook through. When the beans are just soft, add the currants, ground fennel seeds and cinnamon and mix. Add the couscous, mix briefly and then add 100ml (3½fl oz) water. Stir well until the water has been absorbed by the couscous, then set aside for 5 minutes.

Mix the couscous well again to fluff it up. Stir in the chopped herbs and fennel fronds, if any, and serve hot or at room temperature with the salmon wrapped in vine leaves, and harissa and lemon wedges.

Fibre rating: MEDIUM

Per serving: 3.6g fibre, 385 kcals, 25g fat, 4g saturated fat, 1.12g sodium

Tuna niçoise with a pulse

To make this as a starter, you might want to increase the amount of fish a little. I have sometimes made this dish adding 150g unpeeled new potatoes to increase the fibre and carbohydrate content. **Serves 2 as a main dish or 4 as a starter or light lunch**

150g (5oz) cooked chickpeas
2 heaped tablespoons coarsely chopped or torn basil
2 tablespoons lemon juice
4 tablespoons extra virgin olive oil, plus extra for drizzling
Salt and freshly ground pepper
150g (5oz) green beans

125g (4½oz) cherry tomatoes, halved
50g (2oz) rocket or other green salad leaf
310g (11oz) fresh tuna steak
75g (3oz) black olives or 4 heaped teaspoons tapenade
Lemon wedges, to serve

Mix the chickpeas with the basil, 1 tablespoon of the lemon juice and 2 tablespoons of the olive oil. Season with pepper, mix and leave to marinate.

Cook the green beans in boiling water for a few minutes until just tender, drain well and place in a large salad bowl. Add the tomatoes and rocket, season with salt and pepper and add the remaining lemon juice and olive oil, but don't mix until ready to serve or the rocket will become limp.

Heat a griddle pan or grill and drizzle a dash of oil on both sides of the tuna steak. Cook briefly, as tuna tastes delicious served raw in the middle like rare roast beef: allow about 1 minute each side, depending on how thick the tuna is. Remember that it will carry on cooking after it is removed from the heat. Cook through if you prefer. Break the tuna in half if you want to see whether it's cooked – you can always serve two pieces arranged one above the other. Season with salt and pepper.

Add the chickpeas to the salad; mix and divide between serving plates. Place the tuna on top of the salad and serve with olives or a dollop of tapenade on top and a wedge of lemon to squeeze over.

Fibre rating: HIGH
Per serving (main dish): 7g fibre, 564 kcals, 35g fat, 6g saturated fat, 1.02g sodium

Scallop salad with olives, broccoli and beans

Serve with toast or whole new potatoes to include some carbohydrate and fibre in the menu. You could increase the scallops if you wanted to make a more substantial dish. **Serves 4**

150g (5oz) broccoli, cut into florets
150g (5oz) green beans, topped and tailed
175g (6oz) broad beans (picked weight), podded
1 red pepper, deseeded and cut into small thin strips
16 good-quality black olives
4 tablespoons extra virgin olive oil, plus extra for drizzling

2 tablespoons lemon juice or vinegar
Salt and freshly ground black pepper
8 large scallops, total weight 350–400g (12–14oz)
2 heaped tablespoons chopped fresh herbs, such as basil and parsley

Steam the broccoli and green beans until just cooked. Boil the broad beans in water until just cooked. Remove some of the pale outer skin from the broad beans if very large: the contrast in colour works well. Place all the cooked vegetables in a bowl and add the red pepper, olives, olive oil and lemon juice or vinegar. Season with salt and pepper and mix briefly.

Heat a griddle or frying pan and drizzle a little oil over the scallops. Season with salt and pepper and cook briefly on both sides for about 2–4 minutes, depending on their size.

Mix the herbs with the vegetables and serve straight away on one large or four individual plates with the scallops on top.

Fibre rating: HIGH
Per serving: 5.3g fibre, 271 kcals, 14g fat, 2g saturated fat, 0.55g sodium

Grilled polenta with prawns, venetian style

If you don't like polenta, the prawns are delicious with simply boiled potatoes or even pasta, but less authentic! Try to find good-quality polenta which is unrefined as opposed to instant and has a higher fibre content. **Serves 4**

150g (5oz) polenta

Salt and freshly ground black pepper

3 tablespoons extra virgin olive oil, plus extra for the polenta

250g (9oz) podded broad beans (fresh or frozen)

200g (7oz) podded peas (fresh or frozen)

1 small onion, chopped

1 large garlic clove, chopped

250g (9oz) ripe tomatoes, diced

2 tablespoons dry white vermouth

2 heaped tablespoons basil, chopped or torn

400g (14oz) peeled large raw prawns

To make the polenta, bring 700ml (1¼ pints) water to the boil with a good pinch of salt and slowly pour in the polenta. Mix with a whisk until it thickens, then stir periodically with a wooden spoon for 40 minutes over a gentle heat until cooked. Follow manufacturer's instructions if using instant. Pour on to a flat plate and leave to cool.

Just before serving, heat a griddle. Cut the polenta into strips or triangles and lightly smear the pieces with olive oil. (You might not need to use all the polenta). Cook on a high heat on both sides until the polenta lifts off easily. Keep warm.

Cook the broad beans and peas separately in boiling water until tender. The pale outer skin of large broad beans can be quite tough, so remove it, revealing the darker inner bean. This will reduce the final quantity, so perhaps remove the skins for just half the beans or only the large ones. Set aside.

Cook the onion in 2 tablespoons of the olive oil for 5 minutes, until soft. Add the garlic and cooked broad beans and peas. Season with salt and pepper and mix briefly. Add the diced tomatoes and cook until they reduce into a thick sauce.

Add the vermouth and cook a minute more. Add the basil, then transfer to a bowl.

Rinse the pan, add the remaining olive oil and cook the prawns on a medium-high heat for about 3–5 minutes on both sides, depending on their size, until golden brown. Add the bean mixture and mix briefly.

Place the grilled polenta on serving plates with the prawn mixture and serve straight away.

Fibre rating: HIGH

Per serving: 7g fibre, 383 kcals, 12g fat, 2g saturated fat, 0.8g sodium

5 Meat

Venison stir-fry with courgettes and mushrooms

Courgettes and mushrooms are low-fibre vegetables, so if you need more high-fibre vegetables try mangetout and peppers. Venison is delicious and is a relatively low-fat meat, but beef or pork also work well. Serve with white or brown rice. **Serves 4**

400g (14oz) lean venison haunch or fillet
50g (2oz) carrots
150g (5oz) shiitake, oyster or chestnut mushrooms
100g (3½oz) courgettes
2 tablespoons sunflower oil
½ teaspoon Chinese five spice (optional)

2 garlic cloves, sliced
1 heaped teaspoon finely grated or chopped fresh ginger
2 tablespoons soy sauce
2 heaped tablespoons coarsely chopped coriander

Prepare all the ingredients before cooking as stir-frying is a quick cooking process and you need all ingredients at hand.
Cut the venison into thin strips. Peel the carrots then, still using the peeler, peel the carrot into long, thin strips. Cut the mushrooms into small or thin strips. Coarsely grate the courgettes.
Heat 1 tablespoon of the sunflower oil in a large wok over a high heat. Add the venison strips and the Chinese five spice, if using, and brown the meat quickly on both sides for about 1 minute. As soon as it is cooked, remove from the wok and set aside.
Heat the remaining sunflower oil and add the garlic and ginger, cooking briefly. Add the carrots, mushrooms and courgettes and cook for a further 2 minutes, stirring frequently.
When the vegetables are just cooked, add the soy sauce, coriander and venison. Mix briefly and serve straight away.

Fibre rating: LOW
Per serving: 0.7g fibre, 186 kcals, 8g fat, 2g saturated fat, 0.35g sodium

Garam masala duck breasts

A simple dish to prepare (see picture on page 96). Delicious with Saffron and Raisin Rice (see page 128) or a chickpea salad for extra fibre. Use ready-prepared garam masala if you wish, though home-made is far superior. **Serves 2 as a main dish or 4 as a starter**

125g (4½oz) low-fat plain yogurt
1 heaped teaspoon cornflour
2 large skinless duck breasts, about 310g (11oz) total weight
1 tablespoon coarsely chopped fresh coriander, to serve

For the garam masala
1 teaspoon cardamom seeds (removed from pods)
1 small cinnamon stick, broken up
1 teaspoon cloves
1 teaspoon black peppercorns
2 teaspoons cumin seeds
2 teaspoons coriander seeds

To make the garam masala, grind all the ingredients in a spice grinder or pestle and mortar until fine. This can be prepared in advance. You will not need all of it for this recipe, but it keeps well in a sealed container for several months.
Put the yogurt, cornflour and 2 heaped teaspoons garam masala in a shallow bowl and mix well. Place the duck breasts in the bowl and turn to cover completely in the marinade. Cover the bowl and leave in the fridge for 4 hours or overnight (the flavour will improve if left overnight).
Remove the duck from the fridge 30 minutes before cooking. Heat a griddle to medium high or a grill to high. Remove most of the yogurt mixture from the duck and cook the breasts for about 8–10 minutes, turning over halfway through. Cook a little longer if you prefer your duck cooked through. Set aside to rest for 5 minutes before serving.
Place the yogurt mixture in a saucepan and gently bring to the boil. Cook briefly and add a dash of water if the mixture is too thick.
Serve the duck with the warm yogurt dressing on top and a scattering of coriander for colour.

Fibre rating: LOW
Per serving (main course): 0g fibre, 270 kcals, 11g fat, 3g saturated fat, 0.21g sodium

Quail stuffed with apricots and wild mushrooms

To make this dish with poussin instead of quail, allow one small poussin per person and increase the cooking time. Game and poultry work well with dried fruits and apricots are a good source of fibre. **Serves 4**

2 tablespoons olive oil

1 large red onion, finely chopped

1 large garlic clove, chopped

1 heaped tablespoon chopped sage

20g (¾oz) dried wild mushrooms such as porcini, soaked in just enough hot water to cover

50g (2oz) dried apricots, chopped

100g (3½oz) cooked pearl barley

1 teaspoon grated or chopped fresh or stem ginger

Salt and freshly ground black pepper

8 quail or 4 small poussin

Green bean and rocket salad, to serve (optional)

Heat the olive oil in a saucepan and gently cook the onion and garlic for about 10 minutes until soft and transparent, then add the sage.

Drain the mushrooms, reserving the soaking water, chop them and add to the onions along with the apricots. Cook for a minute, then add the mushroom water, discarding any sediment. Add the cooked pearl barley and ginger and simmer gently until all the mushroom liquid has evaporated. Season with salt and pepper. Set aside to cool. (Never stuff a bird with warm stuffing unless cooking it straight away.) The stuffing can be prepared in advance and stored in the fridge, but remove it from the fridge 15 minutes before using.

Place a small roasting tray in the oven and preheat to 200°C/400°F/gas mark 6. Stuff the quail with the mushroom mixture. Tie the legs together to keep the stuffing from falling out, place breast up on the roasting tray and season with salt and pepper.

Roast the birds for 10 minutes. Turn them over and place back in the oven for a further 10 minutes. Turn the heat down to 180°C/350°F/gas mark 4, turn the birds breast up again and cook for a further 5–10 minutes. Add a dash of water at this stage to prevent the juices from evaporating. Remove from the oven and leave to rest for 10–15 minutes before eating.

Cut the quail in half lengthways, pour the cooking juices on top and serve with a green bean and rocket salad. If there is any stuffing not used, it can be reheated at the last minute and served alongside.

Fibre rating: LOW

Per serving, not including green bean and rocket salad: 1.3g fibre, 424 kcals, 26g fat, 6g saturated fat, 0.59g sodium

Pot-roasted beef brisket

This can be used as the basis for various dishes including Beef and Potato Hash on page 48, in which case the extra can be enjoyed another day for a main course with mustard and simply roasted vegetables. Plain rather than salted brisket is used for a subtler flavour. **Serves 6–8**

1.5kg (3lb 5oz) beef brisket, unrolled
200ml (7fl oz) red wine
1 teaspoon black peppercorns
1 tablespoon sea salt
2 small star anise or 1 level teaspoon Chinese five spice (optional)
2 large carrots, halved
1 large onion, quartered
4 garlic cloves

Preheat the oven to 180°C/350°F/gas mark 4. Place the beef in a casserole or high-sided roasting tin.

Pour over the wine, peppercorns, salt and star anise, if using. Scatter over the vegetables and just enough hot water to submerge the beef slightly. (You want to half-steam the meat, not boil it or dry it out.)

Cover with a lid or foil and cook in the oven for about 3 hours. The beef should be soft and tender and flake easily. Once it is cooked, leave to rest for 30 minutes.

Fibre rating: LOW
Per serving (6 people): 0.9g fibre, 596 kcals, 28g fat, 11g saturated fat, 0.94g sodium

Persian chicken with rice

This is a form of pilaf or pilaw – a Middle Eastern method of cooking rice, which involves coating it in oil and spices before cooking it in stock. This dish goes well with a simple cucumber and yogurt salad and can be served as part of a southern Mediterranean buffet. **Serves 4**

4 tablespoons extra virgin olive oil
1 medium onion, finely chopped
100g (3½oz) cashew nuts
4 x chicken thighs, skinned, boned, and cut into small cubes (or use chicken breasts for a lower fat version)
1 heaped teaspoon cumin seeds, lightly crushed
2 garlic cloves, finely chopped
Salt and freshly ground black pepper
75g (3oz) dried cranberries
6 cardamom pods
1 cinnamon stick
250g (9oz) brown basmati rice
1 teaspoon ground allspice
Large pinch of saffron, soaked in 2 tablespoons water or chicken stock
500ml (18fl oz) fresh chicken stock or water
2 tablespoons chopped coriander

Heat the olive oil in a large saucepan or deep frying pan, add the onion and cashew nuts and cook on a medium heat until the onion is soft and the nuts have infused in the oil. Increase the heat a little, add the chicken pieces and cumin seeds and cook for about 5 minutes until the chicken is lightly browned, stirring occasionally so all sides are cooked. Add the garlic at this point to prevent it from burning, season with salt and pepper and stir briefly for 1 minute.

Add the cranberries, cardamom, cinnamon stick, rice, allspice and saffron and briefly mix all the ingredients together. Then add the chicken stock, giving a final stir, cover with a lid and cook the mixture at a gentle simmer for about 10–15 minutes until the rice is cooked and the liquid has evaporated.

Serve with the chopped coriander scattered on top. Remember that the cardamom and cinnamon are left whole to infuse their flavour into the dish and should not be eaten: you might want to remind your guests of this before serving!

Fibre rating: MEDIUM
Per serving: 3.1g fibre, 576 kcals, 27g fat, 5g saturated fat, 0.65g sodium

Meatballs with chickpeas
These are often called kofta meatballs and are traditional Morocco fare. I have included chickpeas in the recipe, but other pulses such as borlotti or flageolet beans can be substituted. Serving with wholemeal pitta bread will increase the fibre. **Serves 4**

1 heaped teaspoon cumin seeds

1 heaped teaspoon coriander seeds

1 large garlic clove, crushed with salt

500g (18oz) lean minced beef

2 heaped tablespoons fresh wholemeal breadcrumbs

1 medium egg, beaten (optional)

1 tablespoon coarsely chopped fresh coriander

Salt and freshly ground black pepper

2 tablespoons olive oil

400g (14oz) tin cooked chickpeas, drained and rinsed

400g (14oz) tin chopped tomatoes

To serve (optional)

Low-fat bio yogurt, coarsely chopped fresh coriander and warm pitta bread

Dry-roast the cumin and coriander in a small frying pan or saucepan until light golden brown – watch carefully as they can burn very easily. Remove and grind using a pestle and mortar or spice grinder. (You can use ready-ground spices but the smoky aroma is lost). Add the spices and puréed garlic to the minced meat and mix with the breadcrumbs, egg, if using, coriander, salt and pepper. Mix well and roll into 24 small balls about the size of a walnut.

Heat the oil in a large sauté or frying pan and cook the meatballs on a medium heat, turning frequently, until coloured all over. Cook in batches if need be. Drain any fat from the pan with a spoon and discard.

Add the chickpeas to the meatballs. Mix briefly, reduce the heat and cook for a few minutes. Add the tomatoes and simmer gently until all the liquid is reduced, making a sweet-flavoured sauce. Leave to rest for at least 10 minutes off the heat, then add a dash of water to loosen slightly, while still leaving a thick sauce. Reheat briefly at this stage if necessary.

Serve with a dollop of yogurt and a sprinkling of coriander; warm pitta or wholemeal bread is good for mopping up the leftover juices.

Fibre rating: MEDIUM
Per serving including egg, not including serving suggestion: 3.6g fibre, 353 kcals, 19g fat, 6g saturated fat, 0.62g sodium

Middle eastern lamb wrapped in cabbage leaves

I always love recipes that use up leftovers and this is much more glamorous than shepherd's pie! Sumac is a spice that can be easily found in any Middle Eastern grocery store. **Serves 4**

250g (9oz) cooked leg of lamb, trimmed of any fat
50g (2oz) bulghur wheat
50g (2oz) pinenuts or hazelnuts, roasted in a medium oven for 10 minutes and coarsely chopped
50g (2oz) spring onions, finely chopped
2 heaped tablespoons coarsely chopped flat-leaf parsley
2 heaped tablespoons coarsely chopped mint
1 red pepper, deseeded and diced
Juice of 2 large lemons (10 tablespoons)
1 tablespoon sumac (or grated lemon zest if unavailable)
Salt and freshly ground black pepper
About 16–20 cabbage leaves

If you have a mincer, mince the lamb on a coarse setting; otherwise finely chop it. Don't be tempted to use a food processor, because this will result in a purée.

Soak the bulghur wheat in enough boiling water just to cover. Leave for 10 minutes until it softens, drain in a colander for a few minutes if the water has not all been soaked up, and press briefly to remove any excess water.

Place the minced lamb in a bowl and add the bulghur wheat, nuts, spring onions, parsley, mint, red pepper, lemon juice, sumac or lemon zest, salt and pepper. Taste for seasoning and leave to infuse. This can be prepared in advance.

Bring a large saucepan of water to the boil. Add the cabbage leaves and blanch them for about 5 minutes until just soft. Refresh them in cold water and leave to drain well.

This dish can be served as ready-made rolls, or you can serve separately and let people wrap the lamb themselves. Place a spoonful of the lamb mixture in the middle of each leaf and wrap up. Try to get the right proportion of lamb to cabbage, so the cabbage does not overpower the meat.

Fibre rating: MEDIUM
Per serving: 4.7g fibre, 319 kcals, 15g fat, 3g saturated fat, 0.36g sodium

Mediterranean chicken and prune

stew *Prunes have a reputation for being too wholesome but their sweet, rich flavour is perfect for any meat stew and gives colour to the sauce as well. Serve with Wholesome Mashed Tatties (page 118) and steamed green vegetables for extra fibre.* **Serves 4**

4 large chicken thighs, skinned and boned, about 375g (13oz) total weight
2 tablespoons extra virgin olive oil
4 rashers pancetta or smoked bacon, diced
1 medium onion, quartered and sliced
4 medium carrots, cut in half lengthways and sliced at an angle

Salt and freshly ground black pepper
2 garlic cloves, sliced
1 heaped tablespoon chopped thyme or rosemary
125g (4½oz) stoned prunes
1 heaped teaspoon cornflour, mixed with 1 tablespoon water
350ml (12fl oz) chicken stock

Cut the chicken thighs into large cubes. Pour the olive oil into a large sauté pan or flameproof casserole and cook the chicken on a medium-high heat until golden brown on all sides. Remove from the pan, leaving any oil behind, and set aside.

Add the pancetta or bacon to the pan and brown lightly. Add the onion and carrots and cook gently for 10 minutes, stirring periodically. Season with salt and pepper and add the garlic and herb. Stir and cook for a minute more.

Return the chicken and add the prunes, mix briefly and add the cornflour paste and chicken stock. Bring to a simmer, cover with a lid and cook gently for 20 minutes.

Fibre rating: MEDIUM
Per serving: 3.6g fibre, 347 kcals, 16g fat, 4g saturated fat, 0.69g sodium

Beef and butter bean stew with

peppers *Other pulses such as cannellini beans can be substituted for the butter beans. Always wash beans well to drain them of the cooking water which causes most of the flatulence associated with beans and pulses.* **Serves 4**

2 tablespoons extra virgin olive oil
375g (13oz) lean stewing beef, cubed
1 medium onion, chopped
1 medium carrot, chopped (unpeeled)
1 celery stick, chopped
2 small red or green peppers, deseeded and cut into chunks
2 garlic cloves, chopped

450g (1lb) butter beans, rinsed and drained
Salt and freshly ground black pepper
75–100ml (3–3½fl oz) sherry vinegar or red wine vinegar
1 heaped teaspoon cornflour
400ml (14fl oz) beef stock or water
Warm crusty bread, to serve (optional)

Preheat the oven to 150°C/300°F/gas mark 2.

Pour the olive oil into a flameproof casserole and heat to medium high. Seal the beef in the oil, turning once, until golden brown. Remove from the casserole and set aside.

Add the onion, carrot, celery, peppers and garlic to the casserole and cook gently for 10 minutes, stirring occasionally. Add the butter beans and beef, mix briefly, then season with salt and pepper. Mix the cornflour with the vinegar and stock or water and add to casserole. Stir, then cover with a lid and place in the oven. Cook for about 1½–2 hours, until the beef is tender.

Serve with warm crusty bread, either wholemeal or white, depending on your fibre requirements.

Fibre rating: HIGH
Per serving not including bread: 5g fibre, 259 kcals, 10g fat, 2g saturated fat, 1.07g sodium

Grilled chicken sandwich on pumpernickel bread with roast peppers and houmous

Pumpernickel bread is made from very coarse meal rye flour. It is also a very high-fibre bread, so a little can go a long way! **Serves 2**

150g (5oz) chicken breast

1 red pepper

4 slices pumpernickel bread (check the fibre table on page 24 if you need to use a lower fibre bread)

2 heaped tablespoons houmous

Salt and freshly ground black pepper

2 dill or flat-leaf parsley sprigs (optional)

2 large watercress sprigs

Preheat the grill to medium-high and grill the chicken breast for about 10 minutes, depending on the thickness. When it is cooked through, set aside to rest.

Grill the pepper, place in a plastic bag to loosen the skin, then remove the skin, halve the pepper and remove the seeds.

Lightly toast the pumpernickel bread on both sides, being careful not to break it as it's quite fragile. Place a piece on each serving plate. Smear the bread with houmous. Thinly slice the chicken breast and divide between the slices of bread. Lay a red pepper half over the chicken. Season with salt and pepper, then place a sprig of dill or parsley, if using, and some watercress on top.

Cover with the remaining pumpernickel and serve straight away. Cut in half with a sharp serrated knife for best results.

Fibre rating: HIGH

Per serving: 7.2g fibre, 359 kcals, 10g fat, 1g saturated fat, 0.73g sodium

6 Vegetables and Tofu

Stir-fried asparagus with sesame seeds

A quick and easy recipe to use when asparagus is in season and you are bored of eating it just boiled with olive oil or butter. It can be made more elaborate by adding ginger or other vegetables. Serve with stir-fried noodles or steamed rice. **Serves 2**

200g (7oz) trimmed asparagus
1 tablespoon sunflower oil
1 heaped tablespoon sesame
  seeds
1 garlic clove, thinly sliced
1 tablespoon oyster sauce
1 tablespoon soy sauce

Cut the asparagus at an angle into thin strips, so that it is easier to cook in a wok.

Heat the oil in a wok and add the asparagus and sesame seeds. Stir and cook for 2 minutes. Add the garlic and cook for 1 further minute.

Add the oyster sauce and soy sauce, stirring so that asparagus briefly steams in the liquid. Place on plates and serve straight away at room temperature.

Fibre rating: LOW
Per serving: 2.2g fibre, 120 kcals, 10g fat, 1g saturated fat, 0.67g sodium

Asparagus and red onion tart

If asparagus is not in season, substitute grilled red peppers. If only fat asparagus is available, cut in half lengthways. Use wholemeal pastry if you wish to increase the fibre content. **Serves 4 as a main dish or 6 as a starter**

250g (9oz) shortcrust pastry
4 medium red onions,
  quartered and finely sliced
2 garlic cloves, thinly sliced
1 heaped tablespoon chopped
  thyme
2 tablespoons olive oil
2 tablespoons balsamic
  vinegar
200g (7oz) trimmed thin
  asparagus
125g (4½oz) ricotta cheese
Salt and freshly ground black
  pepper

Roll out the pastry to 3mm (⅛in) thickness and use to line a 24cm (9½in) metal tart tin. Press the pastry gently into the tin, trimming the edge, but making sure that it comes a little above the side of the tin, so that when it cooks it doesn't shrink too much. Leave to rest in the fridge for about 15 minutes.

Preheat the oven to 180°C/350°F/gas mark 4.

Gently cook the onions, garlic and thyme in the olive oil for about 20 minutes until soft and lightly caramelised, stirring periodically. Add the balsamic vinegar and cook until it has completely reduced into the onions. Set aside.

Cook the asparagus in salted boiling water for a few minutes, until just tender. Refresh in cold water. Dry on kitchen paper.

Prick the pastry base with a fork and bake blind for about 15 minutes. Once the pastry is a light golden brown and completely cooked remove from the oven. Increase the oven to 200°C/400°F/gas mark 6. Place the onion mixture in the pastry case, spreading it out evenly. Trim the asparagus to fit like wheel spokes on top of the onion mixture, place in position and dollop the ricotta all over. Season with salt and pepper and put back in the oven for another 5–10 minutes to brown the ricotta lightly. Be careful not to burn the edges of the pastry – turn the heat down a little if your oven is fierce. Serve warm.

Fibre rating: LOW
Per serving (starter): 2.7g fibre, 294 kcals, 18g fat, 6g saturated fat, 0.38g sodium

Stir-fried tofu with peppers and black bean sauce

Good Oriental food stores sell fermented black beans which make for a more authentic sauce. If not, black bean sauce is more easily available, being stocked by most big supermarkets. Serve with steamed white rice. **Serves 4**

- 285g (10½oz) tofu, drained on kitchen paper for 10 minutes
- 2 tablespoons sunflower oil
- 2 large red peppers, deseeded and cut into triangular shapes
- 175g (6oz) mangetout, sugar snap peas or snow peas
- 3 large spring onions, sliced
- 2 garlic cloves, chopped or grated
- 2 heaped teaspoons fresh chopped or grated ginger
- 1 tablespoon hoisin sauce
- 1 heaped tablespoon black bean sauce or fermented black beans
- 1 teaspoon chilli paste (optional)
- 4 tablespoons Chinese wine or sake, sherry or water

After preparing the vegetables, cut the tofu into 2.5cm (1in) cubes.

Heat the sunflower oil in a large wok and cook the tofu on a medium-high heat until golden brown on all sides. Set aside to drain on kitchen paper.

Add the peppers, mangetout and spring onions to the wok and cook for 2 minutes, stirring frequently. Add the garlic and ginger and cook for 1 further minute.

Finally add the hoisin sauce, black bean sauce or fermented black beans, chilli paste, if using, Chinese wine or alternative and 50ml (2fl oz) water. Cook briefly, then add the tofu, turning the heat down to low. Mix all the ingredients together, cooking the sauce further until thick, and serve.

Fibre rating: LOW
Per serving: 2.6g fibre, 170 kcals, 9g fat, 1g saturated fat, 0.21g sodium

Tofu curry with pumpkin and broccoli

If kaffir lime leaves are hard to find, you can substitute lemon grass. Both have a fragrant acidity to counteract the richness of the coconut milk. Substitute carrots for the pumpkin to increase the fibre content of the dish. **Serves 4**

- 285g (10½oz) tofu (beancurd), drained on kitchen paper for 10 minutes
- 2 tablespoons sunflower oil
- 225g (8oz) pumpkin (peeled weight), cut into 2.5cm (1in) cubes
- 175g (6oz) broccoli, cut into small pieces, including the stems
- 1 heaped teaspoon coriander seeds
- 1 heaped teaspoon cumin seeds
- 400ml (14oz) tin coconut milk
- 1 medium tomato, diced
- ½–1 teaspoon red curry paste
- 2 tablespoons Thai fish sauce
- 3 kaffir lime leaves or 2 medium lemon grass sticks, cut into chunks
- 100g (3½oz) baby spinach leaves
- 1 tablespoon lime juice
- 2 heaped tablespoons coarsely chopped Thai basil or coriander
- Steamed jasmine rice, to serve (optional)

Cut the tofu into 2.5cm (1in) cubes.

Heat the sunflower oil in a large wok and fry the tofu on a medium-high heat until golden brown on all sides. Set aside to drain on kitchen paper.

Add the pumpkin and broccoli to the wok with the coriander and cumin. Cook for a minute to seal the vegetables in the oil and lightly roast the spices. Add the coconut milk, tomato, red curry paste, fish sauce and lime leaves or lemon grass. Mix well and simmer gently for 15 minutes until the vegetables are just tender.

Add the tofu, spinach, lime juice and basil or coriander. Mix well, cooking the spinach until just wilted, then serve straight away with steamed jasmine rice.

Fibre rating: LOW
Per serving not including rice: 2.4g fibre, 164 kcals, 10g fat, 1g saturated fat, 0.76g sodium

Oriental steamed tofu with mushrooms and greens

Several tofu recipes have been included in this book as it is a lean source of protein, rich in calcium. But it has little fibre so is best when you need low fibre in your diet. **Serves 4 as a starter or light meal**

285g (10½oz) tofu (beancurd), drained on kitchen paper for 10 minutes
2 tablespoons sunflower oil
200g (7oz) fresh shiitake or straw mushrooms
1 garlic clove, sliced
310g (11oz) sprouting broccoli or mustard greens
Steamed rice, to serve (optional)

For the marinade
1 heaped teaspoon finely grated fresh ginger
1 garlic clove, finely chopped or grated
1 heaped teaspoon miso paste
2 tablespoons soy sauce
2 tablespoons sake, sherry or dry vermouth

To make the marinade, mix all the ingredients together in a bowl.

Cut the tofu into 2.5cm (1in) cubes and add to the marinade, carefully coating the tofu without breaking it. Leave for a couple of hours in the fridge.

Remove the tofu from the marinade and steam for 5 minutes, then set aside in the steamer to keep warm.

Heat the sunflower oil in a large wok and cook the mushrooms with the garlic until soft. Add the broccoli or greens and a dash of the water from the steamed tofu and cook gently with a lid on (or covered with foil) for 15 minutes, stirring periodically. When the greens are just tender, place these and the mushrooms on a warmed plate.

Put the marinade ingredients into the wok, cook briefly, then add a dash of the tofu steaming water to loosen the sauce if need be. Set aside.

Place the tofu on top of the mushrooms and greens and drizzle the hot sauce on top. Serve straight away with steamed rice.

Fibre rating: LOW
Per serving not including rice: 1.8g fibre, 160 kcals, 9g fat, 1g saturated fat, 0.1g sodium

Thai noodles with tofu and vegetables

Traditionally this recipe requires preserved turnip, found in any good Thai food shop, though it is not essential. Include 1 heaped tablespoon of it when adding the vegetables, if you wish. **Serves 4**

250g (9oz) tofu, drained on kitchen paper for 10 minutes
175g (6oz) rice noodles
2 tablespoons sunflower oil
2 eggs
2 yellow peppers, cut into triangular shapes
3 large spring onions, sliced
1 heaped tablespoon preserved turnip (optional)

2 garlic cloves, chopped
1 teaspoon chilli paste (optional)
1 tablespoon tamarind paste (or juice of 1 large lime)
3 tablespoons Thai fish sauce
25g (1oz) ready-salted peanuts, coarsely chopped
2 heaped tablespoons coarsely chopped coriander or Thai basil

Cut the tofu into 2.5cm (1in) cubes.

Place the noodles in a large bowl or saucepan and pour boiling water over them. Leave for about 3–5 minutes until they loosen up and are al dente. Stir them around in the water to prevent them sticking together. Drain, refresh in cold water and drain again, leaving a little water to stop them sticking.

Have all the prepared vegetables and other ingredients to hand before you start as the rest of the dish will be cooked rapidly.

Heat the sunflower oil in a large wok on a medium-high heat and add the cubed tofu, lightly browning on all sides for a few minutes. Remove and leave to drain on kitchen paper.

Break the eggs into the pan, breaking the yolks. Cook, folding the eggs slightly to break them into large pieces, rather than scrambling them. Push the eggs to the side and add the peppers, spring onions, preserved turnip, garlic and chilli paste, if using, and cook, stirring periodically, for 3 minutes until the peppers are just tender.

Add the tamarind paste and fish sauce, stir briefly, then add the tofu, noodles and peanuts, mixing well. Finally add coriander or basil and serve straight away.

Fibre rating: LOW
Per serving: 1.9g fibre, 385 kcals, 15g fat, 2g saturated fat, 0.96g sodium

Potato-base pizza with courgettes, olives and ricotta

A tasty wheat-free alternative to regular pizza. As with any pizza, the toppings can be adapted, they just should need very little time to cook, or be cooked already.

Serves 2 as a main dish or 4 as a starter

2 tablespoons olive oil, plus extra for greasing
1 large baking potato
Salt and freshly ground black pepper
1 large courgette
100g (3½oz) ricotta cheese
50g (2oz) tapenade or 12 large black stoned olives
1 heaped tablespoon chopped basil or thyme
Salad, to serve

Place a large baking tray in the oven and preheat to 200°C/400°F/gas mark 6. Cut a sheet of foil about 36 x 40cm (14 x 16in) and smear with a little olive oil leaving an unoiled border of about 5cm (2in) around the edge.

Peel and thinly slice the potato and arrange on the foil in a rectangular shape, overlapping slightly. Season with salt and pepper and drizzle 1 tablespoon of the oil on top.

Thinly slice the courgette and scatter over, leaving a little gap around the edges as you would on a pizza base. Dollop the ricotta evenly across the top and scatter over the tapenade or olives. If using thyme, sprinkle it on the pizza now (basil should be added after cooking). Finally drizzle over the remaining oil and season with salt and pepper.

Remove the heated baking tray from the oven and carefully place the foil holding the pizza on top. Cook in the oven for about 15–20 minutes until the edges are golden brown and the centre soft and cooked.

Remove from the oven and, if using basil, scatter over the pizza now. Leave to rest for 5 minutes.

Cut into quarters and serve with salad.

Fibre rating: MEDIUM
Per serving (main course): 3.4g fibre, 317 kcals, 19g fat, 5g saturated fat, 1.05g sodium

Leek and yellow pepper bake

Lovely with simply grilled or roasted meat or fish. The latter makes for a particularly easy recipe as the whole meal comes from the oven and needs little assistance. It would also work well with Stuffed Quail (page 99) or Monkfish Kebabs (page 86). **Serves 4**

2 large yellow peppers
350g (12oz) leeks
2 large garlic cloves, quartered
1 tablespoon chopped thyme
3 tablespoons extra virgin olive oil
Salt and freshly ground black pepper

Preheat the oven to 180°C/350°F/gas mark 4.

Cut the peppers in half and discard the stem and seeds. Cut into large wedges.

Cut the leeks in half and cut into 7.5cm (3in) lengths.

Place the vegetables in a large gratin dish and mix with the garlic, thyme, oil, salt and pepper.

Cover with foil and bake in the oven for 20 minutes. Remove the foil and cook for a further 20 minutes, until the vegetables are soft. Serve.

Fibre rating: MEDIUM
Per serving: 4.1g fibre, 128 kcals, 9g fat, 1g saturated fat, 0.3g sodium

Mini pea and potato pasties
The peas can be substituted with other vegetables such as courgettes if you prefer. They should be cooked at the same time as the potatoes. The potatoes can also be peeled if a lower fibre option is needed.

Makes 12 pasties; serves 4–6

500g (18oz) wholemeal or plain shortcrust pastry

1 medium onion, finely chopped

1 large garlic clove, finely chopped

2 tablespoons extra virgin olive oil

200g (7oz) non-waxy potatoes, such as 'King Edward'

Salt and freshly ground black pepper

125g (4½oz) frozen peas

1 heaped tablespoon coarsely chopped fresh mint

2 tablespoons water or milk, to glaze

Roll out the pastry to about 3mm (⅛in) thickness and 33cm (13in) in diameter. Leave to rest in the fridge on a floured plate, folded if necessary, for about 15 minutes.

Cook the onion and garlic in the olive oil for a few minutes. Cut the potatoes into small dice and add to the onion. Season with salt and pepper and cover with a lid. Gently cook the potatoes, stirring frequently, for about 20 minutes until they are soft. Add the frozen peas and mint and cook for a further 5 minutes. Set aside to cool.

Preheat the oven to 200°C/400°F/gas mark 6.

Take the pastry from the fridge and cut it into 12 discs of about 10cm (4in) diameter, rerolling as necessary to use all the trimmings. Rest the pastry again if you have time as this helps prevent cracking and shrinkage when cooking.

To fill the pastry, brush the edge of pastry circles with a little water or milk and place about ½ tablespoon of the pea mixture in the centre of each one. Fold up two sides of the pastry and pinch in the middle to seal, then fold up one other side, creating two seams and press the pastry together. Repeat on the other side so you have a square shape with four sealed lines. Alternatively fold over the pastry and seal down one side to make a half-moon shape.

Place the pasties on a baking tray and brush with a little more water or milk to glaze. Cook in the oven for about 20 minutes until the pastry is cooked and golden brown.

Serve after resting for about 10 minutes. Don't worry if the parcels break their seal – they are just as tasty!

Fibre rating: MEDIUM
Per pasty, with wholemeal pastry: 3.2g fibre, 221 kcals, 14g fat, 4g saturated fat, 0.25g sodium

Grilled aubergines with miso

A very simple recipe. Miso has a wonderful intense taste that is rich, salty and tart. It is a base note to many Japanese recipes and keeps for ages in the fridge once opened. Traditionally red miso is used, but any good miso will work. **Serves 4 as a side dish or starter**

800g (1¾lb) aubergines
Sea salt
2 level tablespoons miso

2 tablespoons mirin or sake,
   sherry or vermouth
2 teaspoons sugar
Black and white sesame seeds

Cut the aubergines in half lengthways and score the cut sides in a criss-cross pattern, avoiding cutting too deep into the flesh and losing the shape. Sprinkle with salt and leave to sweat for 10 minutes. Rinse in water and squeeze dry, then wrap in kitchen paper.

Preheat the grill or oven to medium.

Grill or bake the aubergines for about 15 minutes until completely cooked. Some vegetables can be al dente but not aubergines.

Make the miso paste by mixing the miso with the mirin or alternative alcohol and the sugar. When the aubergines are cooked, smear the miso mixture over the top, so that it is completely covered. Sprinkle with the sesame seeds, covering half with white and the other half with black.

Serve warm, and with plain rice if serving as a light vegetarian main dish.

Fibre rating: MEDIUM
Per serving: 4.2g fibre, 92 kcals, 3g fat, 0g saturated fat, 0.76g sodium

Tofu-sesame dipping sauce with steamed vegetables

This is a tasty dipping sauce to eat with raw or steamed vegetables and is a different way of using tofu. Serve with boiled rice and a grilled piece of chicken for a complete meal. **Serves 4**

285g (10½oz) soft tofu (beancurd), drained for 10 minutes on kitchen paper
50g (2oz) sesame seeds
2 tablespoons rice wine vinegar
2 tablespoons soy sauce

To serve
150g (5oz) broccoli, cut into thin florets
150g (5oz) green beans
200g (7oz) carrots, cut into strips
1 red pepper, deseeded and sliced
Boiled rice (optional)

Place the tofu in a steamer. Bring to the boil, cover with a lid and cook for 10 minutes. A colander over a saucepan of boiling water works just as well if covered.

Toast the sesame seeds in a medium oven or on top of the stove in a frying pan until golden brown. Reserve 1 heaped teaspoon for the garnish and grind the rest in a spice grinder or using a pestle and mortar.

Place the tofu, ground sesame seeds, vinegar and soy sauce in a blender or food processor and blend until smooth. Pour into a serving bowl, and sprinkle with the reserved toasted sesame seeds just before serving.

Serve the vegetables steamed or raw, accompanied by the tofu dressing as a dipping sauce.

Fibre rating: MEDIUM
Per serving not including rice: 4.6g fibre, 174 kcals, 11g fat, 2g saturated fat, 0.14g sodium

Braised fennel with carrots

A simple combination of vegetables that tastes delicious with grilled fish or chicken. Courgettes can be substituted for carrots. Leave the carrots unpeeled to increase the fibre content of the dish and choose organic carrots that have no chemicals sprayed on the skin. **Serves 4**

400g (14oz) bulb fennel
310g (11oz) carrots
3 tablespoons extra virgin olive oil
1 large garlic clove, chopped

Salt and freshly ground black pepper
1 heaped tablespoon chopped basil

Remove any fennel fronds, chop and set aside. Cut the fennel in half lengthways and slice into thin wedges. Cut the carrots in half lengthways and thinly slice at an angle.

Heat the oil in a large sauté pan and add the vegetables and garlic. Season with salt and pepper and cook on a medium-high heat, stirring periodically, for 20 minutes, so the vegetables just catch and brown lightly. Place a lid on the pan, reduce the heat and cook for a further 10–15 minutes, until the vegetables are tender. When lifting the lid to stir, add any condensation from the lid to moisten the vegetables and help them cook further.

When the vegetables are soft, add the basil and the reserved chopped fennel fronds and serve. This dish can be prepared in advance as it reheats well.

Fibre rating: MEDIUM
Per serving: 4.2g fibre, 97 kcals, 8g fat, 1g saturated fat, 0.48g sodium

Wholesome mashed tatties in their skins

A friend prepared mashed potatoes this way for me once, I suspect because she couldn't be bothered to peel all the potatoes. Since I realised that most of a potato's nutrients are just under the skin, I have always made mash at home like this. **Serves 4**

500g (18oz) unpeeled potatoes, any non-waxy variety that is good for mashing

Salt and freshly ground black pepper
50g (2oz) unsalted butter
2 tablespoons milk
Good pinch of grated nutmeg

Cut the potatoes into large chunks – they should not be too small or the mash will become waterlogged.

Cook gently in salted boiling water for about 20 minutes until soft. Drain well and return back to the pan. Add the butter in small pieces and pour in the milk. Season with salt, pepper and nutmeg. Mash to a purée and serve. Delicious with a variety of main courses from this book, such as Mediterranean Chicken and Prune Stew (see page 104).

Variation

For a lower fat recipe, use 75ml (3fl oz) olive oil instead of milk and butter.

Fibre rating: MEDIUM
Per serving: 3.4g fibre, 315 kcals, 11g fat, 7g saturated fat, 0.26g sodium

Braised red cabbage with raisins and orange

Red cabbage is an undervalued vegetable but its bright rich colour works well and looks great with most meats but particularly game and poultry. It would work well with Stuffed Quail (page 99) or Mediterranean Chicken (page 104). **Serves 6**

800g (1¾lb) red cabbage
3 tablespoons olive oil
2 tablespoons dark soft brown sugar
2 medium apples, such as 'Cox's', peeled, cored and cubed

Grated zest and juice of 1 large orange
200g (7oz) raisins or sultanas
Salt and freshly ground black pepper
100ml (3½fl oz) balsamic vinegar

Halve the cabbage, cut out the hard, thick white core and discard, then finely slice. Heat the olive oil in a large pan and gently braise the cabbage on a medium heat for 5 minutes, stirring occasionally. You do not want to brown the cabbage – just glaze it with oil. Add 150ml (5fl oz) water, the sugar, apples, orange zest and juice, raisins or sultanas, and season with salt and pepper. Place a lid on the saucepan and cook gently for about 45 minutes, stirring the cabbage periodically and checking that there is enough liquid to prevent it 'catching' the base of the pan. After the cabbage is just tender, remove the lid from the pan and add the balsamic vinegar. Carry on cooking for another 10 minutes until all the liquid has evaporated and the cabbage has a nice sugary glaze.

Serve immediately or allow to cool and store for up to 4 days in the fridge for reheating as required.

Fibre rating: HIGH
Per serving: 5.2g fibre, 215 kcals, 6g fat, 1g saturated fat, 0.33g sodium

Spinach with sesame sauce japanese style

A simple but interesting way of serving spinach. It goes well with steamed fish or with other Japanese-style recipes in this book, such as Mackerel Simmered in Miso Soup (see page 88).

Serves 4

800g (1¾lb) spinach	1 tablespoon soy sauce
1 teaspoon finely grated fresh ginger	1 tablespoon water or 2 tablespoons chicken stock
1 large garlic clove, finely grated	2 tablespoons black or yellow sesame seeds
1 tablespoon tahini (sesame paste)	

Wash the spinach and trim off any large thick stems, but don't bother if they are thin and not too long. Cook the spinach in a large saucepan, stirring frequently – you will probably not need any more water than is clinging to the leaves. Rinse in cold water to cool and squeeze well so the spinach is not soggy.

Place the ginger and garlic in the bottom of a bowl big enough to hold the spinach as well. Stir the tahini first (as it often separates when left to stand) and add to the bowl along with the soy sauce and water or chicken stock. Mix well and add the spinach.

Mix all the ingredients together, taste for the correct balance of seasoning and serve mounded high on a plate with a scattering of sesame seeds on top.

Fibre rating: HIGH
Per serving: 5.5g fibre, 147 kcals, 11g fat, 1g saturated fat, 0.45g sodium

Roasted winter vegetables with pearl barley

A variety of vegetables can be used for this recipe, including sweet potatoes, celeriac, pumpkin and turnips. It is quite high in fat due to the olive oil used so is best avoided if you are following a low-fat diet. **Serves 4**

150g (5oz) pearl barley	350g (12oz) red onions
5 garlic cloves	350g (12oz) leeks
4 heaped tablespoons chopped sage or thyme, plus 1 small sprig	7 tablespoons extra virgin olive oil
Salt and freshly ground pepper	1 tablespoon lemon juice
400g (14oz) pumpkin	50g (2oz) almonds, toasted in a medium oven for 10
400g (14oz) courgettes	minutes until brown

Rinse the pearl barley, place in a saucepan and cover with water. Bring to the boil, drain and rinse again. Place back in the saucepan with 1 of the garlic cloves, the herb sprig and fresh water to cover. Bring to the boil and simmer gently for 45 minutes–1 hour, making sure there is always enough water to cover the barley. The barley should be just soft. Season with salt, drain and set aside. Reheat if need be just before serving.

Preheat the oven to 200°C/400°F/gas mark 6. Peel the pumpkin and cut it and the courgettes into large wedges. Cut the onions in half or quarters, depending on their size, and the leeks in half, to keep their shape. Mix all the vegetables with the remaining 4 garlic cloves (unpeeled), 3 tablespoons of the olive oil, salt and pepper. Place the vegetables in a roasting tray and roast for about 45 minutes until soft, checking them halfway through the cooking time.

Make a sauce with the chopped sage or thyme, a good pinch of salt, pepper, the lemon juice and the remaining olive oil in a food processor. Set aside.

When the barley and vegetables are cooked, spoon 1 tablespoon of the sage sauce into the barley and season if need be.

Place a spoonful of the barley on each serving plate and arrange a variety of the vegetables on top. Finally drizzle over the rest of the sauce, scatter with almonds and serve.

Fibre rating: HIGH
Per serving: 6.9g fibre, 344 kcals, 29g fat, 4g saturated fat, 0.3g sodium

Roast butternut squash and onions with feta

A lovely vegetarian dish, ideal for a light lunch, evening meal or starter. It can be prepared in advance and assembled just before serving. Other kinds of pumpkin can be used in this recipe. **Serves 6**

1kg (2¼ lb) butternut squash, peeled and deseeded
3 large red onions
8 garlic cloves
1 small bunch sage or rosemary, coarsely chopped
Salt and freshly ground black pepper
5 tablespoons extra virgin olive oil
200g (7oz) feta cheese

To serve
4 wholemeal pitta or Lebanese flatbread, toasted, and salad

Preheat the oven to 180°C/350°F/gas mark 4.
Cut the squash and onions into wedges and place separately on foil-lined baking trays. Scatter over the garlic and sage or rosemary and season with salt and pepper. Drizzle 4 tablespoons of the oil over the vegetables and bake them in the oven for about 30 minutes or until the squash is soft. The onions might take a little longer to cook, so just remove the pumpkin and carry on cooking the onions. Once both vegetables are cooked, set aside. This can be done in advance and the vegetables reheated later.
Preheat the grill to high. Place the vegetables in a gratin dish or on a heat-proof plate. Break the feta into small cubes and sprinkle over the vegetables. Drizzle the remaining tablespoon of olive oil over the feta and grill until the cheese is light golden brown.
Serve with toasted pitta or flat bread and a little salad.

Fibre rating: HIGH
Per serving including wholemeal pitta bread: 6.8g fibre, 400 kcals, 17g fat, 6g saturated fat, 0.72g sodium

Roasted celeriac, tomatoes and olives

A high-fibre vegetable dish to serve with simply grilled or roasted meat to bring fibre into the meal. Great in the autumn or winter when celeriacs are in season. Their mild, sweet flavour contrasts well with the olives and rosemary. **Serves 4**

600g (1¼ lb) celeriac
500g (18oz) ripe tomatoes
16 stoned black olives, halved
1 heaped tablespoon chopped rosemary
2 large garlic cloves, chopped
4 tablespoons extra virgin olive oil
Salt and freshly ground black pepper

Preheat the oven to 200°C/400°F/gas mark 6.
Trim the celeriac, removing the skin, and cut into 2.5cm (1in) cubes. Cut the tomatoes into large chunks and place in a bowl with the celeriac, olives, rosemary, garlic, olive oil, salt and pepper. Mix well.
Place the vegetables in a gratin dish about 38 x 26cm (10 x 26in), so that they are not overcrowded. Bake in the oven for about 45 minutes–1 hour, until the vegetables are golden brown and soft.
Serve with simply grilled meat.

Fibre rating: HIGH
Per serving: 6.2g fibre, 149 kcals, 13g fat, 2g saturated fat, 0.73g sodium

7

Pasta, Rice and Pulses

Pumpkin risotto
This is a really comforting dish which is best in autumn when pumpkins are in season. Use a sweet, flavoursome pumpkin such as butternut squash or a Turkish turban. Avoid the English pumpkins produced for decoration, which are watery and tasteless. **Serves 4**

6 tablespoons extra virgin olive oil

1 medium onion, finely chopped

550g (19oz) pumpkin peeled and cut into small cubes

1 large clove garlic, chopped

750ml (26fl oz) chicken stock, preferably home-made

Pinch of grated nutmeg

2 tablespoons chopped sage

200g (7oz) risotto rice, e.g. arborio or carnaroli

Salt and freshly ground black pepper

100ml (3.5fl oz) dry white vermouth or white wine

25g (1oz) Parmesan cheese, grated

Heat the oil in a thick-based saucepan and gently cook the onion, pumpkin and garlic for about 20 minutes until soft, without colouring. Heat the chicken stock in another saucepan.

Add the nutmeg, sage and rice to the pumpkin and mix briefly. Season with salt and pepper and stir for 1 minute to coat the grains of rice.

Add the vermouth or wine and increase the heat to medium. Keep stirring the rice, and when the liquid has almost absorbed into the rice, start adding the hot stock, a couple of ladles at a time, stirring the rice all the time so that it cooks evenly and releases some of its starch, making a creamy consistency.

Taste the liquid around the rice for enough seasoning after adding the first couple of ladles of stock, while the rice is still absorbing flavour. Add more salt and pepper if need be.

When you have nearly used up the stock, start tasting the rice to prevent overcooking. It is ready when it is 'al dente'. Add more water or stock as necessary but stop cooking the rice as soon as it still has a little texture in the middle of the grain. The consistency of the risotto should be rich and thick like porridge, not too sloppy or too dry. Add half the Parmesan just before serving and hand round the rest separately for sprinkling.

Fibre rating: LOW
Per serving: 1.5g fibre, 403 kcals, 20g fat, 4g saturated fat, 0.89g sodium

Pasta with clams
An attractive informal dinner party dish as the pretty shells are left in. In Italy it wouldn't be the done thing to serve this with cheese as it contains chilli and fish. There is no need to add any extra salt to this dish (apart from to the pasta water) as the clams are salty enough. **Serves 4**

1kg (2¼lb) clams, cleaned and drained

Salt

75ml (3fl oz) white wine

310g (11oz) spaghetti or linguine

4 tablespoons extra virgin olive oil

2 large garlic cloves, finely chopped

1 large red chilli, finely chopped

3 heaped tablespoons coarsely chopped coriander

Rinse the clams in cold water. Leave in the water for a few minutes, then drain well.

Bring a large saucepan of salted water to the boil. Heat a large sauté or frying pan with a lid for the clams.

With all the ingredients to hand, add the clams to the hot sauté pan, pour in the wine and cover with a lid. Cook for about 1 minute until all the clams have opened, then drain in a colander placed over a bowl to collect the juice. (You can cook the clams in batches if your pan is not big enough to fit them all at once.)

Add the pasta to the salted boiling water, stirring well to prevent the strands of pasta sticking together. Cook according to the packet instructions until al dente.

Heat the oil in the empty sauté pan and cook the garlic and chilli briefly, then add the coriander and the clam juice, reserving and discarding any sediment. Cook briefly to concentrate the flavours.

Drain the pasta well, add to the sauté pan off the heat and mix thoroughly. Add the clams at the last minute.

Serve immediately, dividing up the pasta and then the clams for easiest results. Pour any remaining juice over each portion.

Fibre rating: LOW
Per serving: 2.3g fibre, 419 kcals, 13g fat, 2g saturated fat, 1.25g sodium

Red rice with green beans and beetroot

This dish can be served hot or at room temperature as a salad. With its vibrant colours this complements any grilled meat or fish or alternatively can be served as a vegetarian main course. **Serves 4**

200g (7oz) red rice
2 garlic cloves (unpeeled)
Salt and freshly ground black pepper
2 tablespoons extra virgin olive oil
1 medium onion, finely chopped
2 celery sticks, finely chopped

75g (3oz) green beans, topped, tailed and cut into discs
Pinch of ground allspice (optional)
200g (7oz) cooked beetroot (not in vinegar), cut into 1cm (½in) cubes
2 heaped tablespoons coarsely chopped mint

Rinse the rice and then cook in a generous amount of boiling water with the garlic and a pinch of salt for about 40 minutes until soft but with a little nutty bite to it still. Drain well. **Heat** the oil and cook the onion, celery and green beans for about 10 minutes until they are soft. Add the rice and allspice, if using, and mix well. Season with salt and pepper. Add the beetroot and mint at the last minute, mix briefly and serve hot or leave to cool to room temperature.

Fibre rating: MEDIUM
Per serving: 3.4g fibre, 270 kcals, 7g fat, 1g saturated fat, 0.57g sodium

Borlotti bean salad with broccoli, pinenuts and anchovies

This can be a meal in itself or can accompany fish or meat. Serve with warm crusty wholemeal bread for extra fibre. **Serves 2 as a main dish or 4 as a side dish**

150g (5oz) broccoli
25g (1oz) pinenuts, roasted for 10 minutes in medium oven
25g (1oz) tinned anchovies, drained and chopped
400g (14oz) tin borlotti beans, drained and rinsed
2 heaped tablespoons chopped mixed fresh herbs such as parsley, mint and basil

Juice of ½ lemon (1½ tablespoons)
3 tablespoons extra virgin olive oil
Salt and freshly ground black pepper
Wholemeal bread to serve (optional)

Steam or boil the broccoli until just tender. Drain well and place in a large bowl with the pinenuts, anchovies and borlotti beans.
Just before serving add the herbs, lemon juice, olive oil, and season with salt and pepper. Mix well and serve.

Fibre rating: MEDIUM
Per serving (side dish) not including bread: 3.9g fibre, 203 kcals, 14g fat, 2g saturated fat, 0.68g sodium

Saffron and raisin rice
A Middle Eastern recipe where rice is combined with lots of other ingredients, but particularly dried fruits, to give it a sort of sweet and sour flavour. Delicious served with Garam Masala Duck (see page 98). Serves 4–6

250g (9oz) brown basmati rice	2 teaspoons cumin seeds
4 tablespoons extra virgin olive oil	75g (3oz) raisins or currants
1 medium onion, finely chopped	6 whole cardamom pods
	1 small cinnamon stick
100g (3½oz) shelled pistachio nuts or pinenuts	Large pinch of saffron strands, soaked in a little water
	Salt and freshly ground black pepper

Rinse the rice in a bowl of cold water and drain.

Pour the oil into a large saucepan or frying pan, add the onion, nuts and cumin seeds and cook on a medium heat until the onion is soft and the nuts and cumin have infused in the oil. Add the raisins or currants, cardamom, cinnamon stick, rice and saffron and season with salt and pepper. Briefly mix all the ingredients together and add enough water to cover the rice by about 2cm (¾in). Cook at a gentle simmer, covered with a lid, for about 30 minutes.

Remove the pan from the heat and with the lid still sealed tight, leave to steam for another 5 minutes until the rice is cooked and the liquid has evaporated. If need be, remove the lid and gently cook the rice until no liquid remains.

Serve hot or at room temperature.

Fibre rating: MEDIUM
Per serving (4 people): 3.6g fibre, 637 kcals, 27g fat, 4g saturated fat, 0.34g sodium

Thai-style squid and chickpea salad
Pulses are not traditionally used in Thai cooking, but chickpeas work very well with squid and I've always loved how the Thais make refreshing squid salads. So I've fused two great recipes to create a tasty medium-fibre salad. Serves 4

2 medium squid, 800g (1¾lb) total weight	240g (8½oz) cooked chickpeas or 400g (14oz) tin, rinsed and drained
2 tablespoons sunflower oil	Juice of 1 lime (3 tablespoons)
100g (3½oz) spring onions or red onions, thinly sliced	1 tablespoon Thai fish sauce
2 heaped teaspoons finely chopped fresh ginger	2 heaped tablespoons coarsely chopped coriander
2 garlic cloves, finely chopped	150g (5oz) tomatoes, cubed
½ large red chilli, finely chopped (optional)	

Get your fishmonger to gut and clean the squid, removing the skin and wings as well. Cut through the body of the squid to flatten out and wash well, making sure the tentacles have all the grit and sand removed from the suckers. Cut into thin strips and drain well.

Prepare all the ingredients before cooking. Heat the oil in a large wok or sauté pan until hot. Add the drained squid and cook, stirring frequently, for about 1–2 minutes, depending on the thickness. Push to one side and add the onions, ginger, garlic and chilli, if using. Turn the heat down to medium and cook for 1 minute. Add the chickpeas, stirring well, and cook 1 further minute.

Remove the pan from the heat and add the lime juice, fish sauce and coriander. Mix well and tip into a serving bowl, add the tomatoes and serve hot or at room temperature.

Fibre rating: MEDIUM
Per serving: 3.3g fibre, 226 kcals, 9g fat, 1g saturated fat, 0.54g sodium

Buckwheat pasta with spinach, mushrooms and truffle oil

Buckwheat pasta is often used in Italian cooking. Like faro, it's a good substitute for wheat pasta. If you are unable to find truffle oil, use a tablespoon of crème fraîche or creamy goat's cheese instead. **Serves 4**

- 2 tablespoons extra virgin olive oil
- 125g (4½oz) chestnut or shiitake mushrooms
- 1 large garlic clove, chopped
- 1 tablespoon chopped thyme or sage
- 200g (7oz) small leaf spinach
- 310g (11oz) buckwheat or faro pasta
- Salt and freshly ground black pepper
- 2 heaped tablespoons grated Parmesan cheese
- Truffle oil, to serve (optional)

Heat the olive oil in a sauté pan or frying pan and cook the mushrooms until soft. Add the garlic and thyme or sage and cook briefly, then add the spinach in batches, stirring the leaves well until they start to wilt before adding the next batch. Continue until the spinach is just cooked. Add a few tablespoons of water if the spinach becomes too dry. Set aside.

Bring a saucepan of salted water to the boil and cook the pasta according to the packet instructions until 'al dente'. Reserve a small cup of the cooking water and drain the pasta, then add the pasta to the spinach mixture. Mix well, adding a little of the reserved cooking water to stop the pasta from sticking and season with salt and pepper.

Serve straight away sprinkled with Parmesan and a good drizzle of truffle oil.

Fibre rating: MEDIUM
Per serving: 4.7g fibre, 366 kcals, 9g fat, 2g saturated fat, 0.36g sodium

Chickpea stew with aubergines, courgettes and tomatoes

This chickpea stew is even better eaten the next day as the flavours will intensify beautifully. Barley couscous is a good alternative to wheat couscous.

Serves 4

- 350g (12oz) aubergines, cut into 5cm (2in) cubes
- 1 heaped tablespoon coriander seeds
- 1 heaped tablespoon cumin seeds
- 6 tablespoons extra virgin olive oil
- 1 medium onion, quartered and sliced
- 350g (12oz) courgettes, cut into 3cm (1¼in) cubes
- 1 large garlic clove
- Salt and freshly ground black pepper
- 400g (14oz) tin chickpeas, rinsed and drained
- 275g (10oz) tomatoes, skinned and chopped

To serve (optional)
- 2 heaped tablespoons coarsely chopped fresh coriander, couscous and low-fat bio yogurt

Salt the aubergine cubes generously, and leave in a bowl to 'sweat' for 15 minutes. Rinse in cold water to remove the salt and any bitter juices and squeeze dry.

Gently dry-roast the coriander and cumin seeds in a heavy-based pan until they give off an aroma. Grind using a pestle and mortar or spice grinder.

Heat the olive oil into a large frying pan or sauté pan and cook the aubergines on a medium-high heat on all sides, until golden brown and soft. Remove from the pan and set aside to drain.

Cook the onion, courgettes and garlic in the same pan for about 15 minutes until the onion is soft and the courgettes are light golden brown. Season with salt and pepper and add the chickpeas and ground spices. Mix briefly and add the tomatoes. Cover and simmer for a further 15 minutes, until the flavours have amalgamated and the tomatoes reduced a little.

Leave to infuse for at least 15 minutes for a better flavour before serving with chopped fresh coriander, couscous and yogurt.

Fibre rating: HIGH
Per serving not including serving suggestion: 6.2g fibre, 270 kcals, 20g fat, 3g saturated fat, 0.43g sodium

Wild rice and spelt with chestnuts and sesame seeds

A tasty side dish that experiments with unusual starches. Wild rice is in fact a grass as opposed to a 'proper' rice. Buy packets or tins of peeled and cooked chestnuts to make this dish easy to prepare. **Serves 6**

250g (9oz) wild rice
150g (5oz) spelt or faro
2 large garlic cloves
2 tablespoons sesame or sunflower oil

1 medium onion, chopped
2 heaped tablespoons sesame seeds
200g (7oz) cooked peeled chestnuts, coarsely chopped

Boil the rice and spelt together with a pinch of salt and the whole garlic cloves in plenty of water for 45 minutes, until the rice and spelt are cooked but still have a bit of bite. Drain well and remove the skin from the garlic.

Heat the oil in a pan and gently cook the onion for 5 minutes. Add the sesame seeds, mix well and cook for a further 5 minutes, until the onion is soft and the sesame seeds light golden brown. Stir frequently.

Add the chopped chestnuts and mix briefly. Then add the rice and warm through, mixing all the flavours together and breaking up the soft garlic.

Serve hot or at room temperature.

Fibre rating: HIGH
Per serving: 5.2g fibre, 377 kcals, 9g fat, 1g saturated fat, 0g sodium

Faro pasta salad with tomatoes, cannellini beans and basil

Faro pasta is made from spelt, a grain often used in Italian cooking, and is high in fibre. For best results, used shaped pasta rather than strands. They are less gluey so work better in cold pasta salads. **Serves 6**

275g (10oz) fusilli faro pasta
Salt and freshly ground black pepper
125g (4½oz) cooked cannellini beans, rinsed and drained
350g (12oz) tasty tomatoes, cubed

4 tablespoons chopped or torn basil
1 large garlic clove, crushed with salt
3 spring onions, finely chopped
2 tablespoons sherry vinegar
4 tablespoons extra virgin olive oil

Cook the pasta in a large pan of salted boiling water until al dente. Allow about 7 minutes or follow the packet instructions. Drain, refresh under cold water and drain well again.

Place the cannellini beans in a bowl. Add the cubed tomatoes, basil and garlic crushed with salt. Add the spring onions, vinegar and oil and season with pepper and a little more salt if need be. Mix in the pasta, taste for seasoning and leave to infuse for a few minutes before serving.

Fibre rating: HIGH
Per serving: 6.1g fibre, 280 kcals, 9g fat, 1g saturated fat, 0.33g sodium

Lentil salad with bacon and grilled peppers

This is what I call an all-in-one salad because it includes carbohydrate in the form of lentils. Green or Puy lentils are a good alternative to serving rice or potatoes with any dish. They are easy to cook, and can be prepared in advance. **Serves 4**

1 tablespoon extra virgin olive oil

100g (3½oz) smoked bacon or pancetta, cubed

150g (5oz) carrots, finely chopped

1 large celery stick, finely chopped

1 large garlic clove, finely chopped

1 tablespoon chopped rosemary

150g (5oz) Puy or green lentils

To serve

100g (3½oz) small leaf spinach

200g (7oz) endive lettuce, cut in half

3 tablespoons lemon juice

1 tablespoon extra virgin olive oil

Salt and freshly ground black pepper

2 red peppers, grilled, deseeded and cut into strips (optional)

Heat the oil in a saucepan and cook the bacon or pancetta until golden and crispy. Add the carrots, celery, garlic and rosemary and cook gently for about 10 minutes.

Add the lentils, mix briefly, then add 500ml (18fl oz) water. Cover with a lid and simmer gently for about 1–1½ hours until the lentils are cooked and all the water has evaporated.

When you are ready to serve, place the salad leaves on individual serving plates or one large plate. Drizzle over the lemon juice and oil, season with salt and pepper and mix briefly. Scatter over the lentils and top with the strips of red peppers, if using. Serve straight away.

Fibre rating: HIGH

Per serving including peppers: 7.2g fibre, 288 kcals, 13g fat, 3g saturated fat, 0.7g sodium

Puddings

8

Peach and grappa sorbet

The best results are achieved when good tasty peaches are in season. Other summer fruits can be substituted and a different alcohol used. Increase the sugar quantity if the mixture is too acidic or add more fruit purée or lemon juice if too sweet. **Serves 6**

5 heaped tablespoons caster sugar

5 tablespoons grappa or brandy (or water if preferred)

5 large peaches, skinned, stoned and chopped

Juice of 1 large lemon

Place the sugar and alcohol or water in a small saucepan and heat gently until the sugar has dissolved. Set aside.

Put the peaches and lemon juice in a food processor and purée finely. Do not over-purée or the colour of the peaches will deteriorate, though the lemon juice helps to prevent this. Pour the peach purée – there should be about 1 litre (1¼ pints) – into a bowl, add the sugar and alcohol syrup and mix thoroughly.

Place in an ice-cream maker and freeze according to the manufacturer's instructions.

If you don't have an ice-cream maker, place the sorbet in a metal bowl or plastic container and place in the freezer. Remove every 30 minutes, stirring well to churn the sorbet into a creamy consistency Continue this process until it is set.

If not eating straight away, freeze the sorbet immediately as peach juice will oxidize, turning an unattractive brown colour.

Fibre rating: LOW

Per serving: 1.9g fibre, 124 kcals, 0g fat, 0g saturated fat, 0g sodium

Strawberry cheesecake

Quark is a fresh curd cheese made from skimmed milk and, as it has a neutral taste, it is ideal for use in desserts like this one. Quark is used here to keep the fat content down, but you can substitute cream cheese if you feel like being indulgent. **Serves 6**

200g (7oz) digestive biscuits

100g (3½oz) blanched almonds, roasted in a medium oven for 10 minutes

75g (3oz) butter, melted

500g (18oz) quark

2 heaped tablespoons icing sugar, or to taste

Grated zest of 1 orange

275g (10oz) hulled strawberries

1 heaped tablespoon caster or icing sugar

1 tablespoon orange juice

Roughly break up the biscuits and grind in a food processor with half the almonds. Mix in the melted butter. Line a 20cm (8in) springform tin (non-fluted) with clingfilm. Put the biscuit mixture into the tin and press down firmly into the base and push up a little around the sides. Place in the fridge to set for 1 hour.

Place the quark in a bowl. Coarsely chop the remaining almonds and add to the quark along with the icing sugar and orange zest. Taste for sweetness. Place on top of the biscuit base, spreading to cover all edges. Leave to rest in the fridge for another hour before serving.

To make the topping, cut the strawberries in quarters or smaller pieces, depending on their size. Mix with the sugar and orange juice and leave to marinate.

Remove the cheesecake from the tin, carefully peeling off the clingfilm before placing it on a plate. Pour the strawberries over the top of the cheesecake just before serving.

Fibre rating: LOW

Per serving: 2.4g fibre, 449 kcals, 26g fat, 10g saturated fat, 0.31g sodium

Chocolate fridge cake
This is my sophisticated version of the timeless cake. Any dried fruit can be used such as pineapple, pears or apples. If you prefer your puddings sweeter, add 25g (1oz) unrefined sugar when melting the chocolate and butter. But don't buy cheap sweet chocolate! **Serves 6–8**

50g (2oz) hazelnuts
150g (5oz) dried fruit, such as cranberries, apricots and papaya
50ml (2fl oz) brandy or rum

175g (6oz) dark chocolate, 70% cocoa solids, cut into small pieces
75g (3oz) unsalted butter, cubed
75g (3oz) digestive biscuits

Line a 20cm (8in) cake tin generously with cling film, so that it reaches over the sides.

Roast the nuts in a medium-high oven for 10 minutes until golden brown. Chop coarsely and place in a large bowl.

Cut the fruit, if need be, into small pieces and mix with the brandy or rum. Set aside to marinate.

Melt the chocolate and butter in a bowl set over a pan of gently simmering water, making sure the base of the bowl does not touch the water, or in a microwave on medium-high. Mix briefly, being careful not to over-heat the chocolate or it will become grainy, not smooth.

Break the digestive biscuits into small pieces and add to the nuts. Pour over the chocolate mixture and add the dried fruits. Mix well.

Pour the chocolate mixture into the tin, pressing down to keep it compact. Cover the tin with clingfilm, making sure it does not touch the top of the mixture, and place in the fridge for at least 4 hours or overnight until chilled and solid. Serve cool.

Fibre rating: MEDIUM
Per serving (6 people): 3g fibre, 430 kcals, 26g fat, 13g saturated fat, 0.09g sodium

Almond and polenta biscuits with fresh fruit
These easy biscuits are a great way to make a plate of fresh fruit more interesting. I use whole almonds when cooking, because ground almonds tend to go stale more quickly. **Makes 24 small biscuits**

100g (3½oz) blanched almonds
150g (5oz) wholemeal flour
100g (3½oz) caster sugar
100g (3½oz) cornmeal or polenta
Grated zest of 1 orange
2 medium eggs

100ml (3½fl oz) sunflower oil
1 level teaspoon baking powder
To serve
Icing sugar, to decorate (optional)
½ passionfruit and 80g slice pineapple per person

Preheat the oven to 180°C/350°F/gas mark 4.

Place all the ingredients, except the icing sugar and fruit, in a food processor and blend until the nuts are finely ground.

Line two baking trays with baking parchment. Space half tablespoons of the mixture evenly on the prepared trays, forming each into a slightly oval shape, ensuring that there is a slight gap between each to allow them to spread while cooking.

Bake in the oven for 15–20 minutes. Remove from the oven and leave to rest on the tray for a further 10 minutes until cool enough to handle.

Dust the biscuits with a little icing sugar if you wish and serve at room temperature with fresh seasonal fruit.

Fibre rating: MEDIUM
Per 2 biscuits with fruit: 3.1g fibre, 277 kcals, 15g fat, 2g saturated fat, 0.05g sodium

Caramelised pears with walnuts and raisins
A simple pudding which is lovely and warming with the addition of cinnamon and ginger. It can be served with yogurt or a biscuit such as a flapjack which will further increase the fibre content. **Serves 4**

4 large slightly ripe pears, preferably 'Comice'
50g unsalted butter
25g (1oz) unrefined caster sugar
Pinch each of cinnamon and ground ginger
75g (3oz) walnut pieces
50g (2oz) raisins or dried cranberries
2 tablespoons lemon juice
Low-fat bio yogurt, to serve

Cut the pears in quarters and remove the core. In a large frying pan or sauté pan, gently melt the butter and add the sugar. Place the pears on top and sprinkle with the cinnamon and ginger. Bring to a gentle simmer to cook the pears, carefully turning and moving them so all get a light browning. Cover with a lid to half-steam and prevent the sugar browning too quickly before the pears are cooked. Alternatively add a dash of water if using a frying pan. Cook for about 20 minutes, until the fruit is soft.

Carefully remove the pears, one at a time, to a serving plate. Add the walnut pieces and raisins or cranberries to the pan and cook for 5 minutes, stirring to prevent the sugar from crystallising. (Alternatively the walnuts can be toasted in a medium oven for 10 minutes and added to the pears at the end.) Add the lemon juice (this can be added earlier if the butter has been absorbed and the sugar is starting to caramelise).

Cover the pears with the nuts and dried fruit and serve while still warm with a dollop of yogurt.

Fibre rating: HIGH
Per serving including yogurt: 5.9g fibre, 386 kcals, 24g fat, 8g saturated fat, 0.04g sodium

Blackcurrant fool
A simple pudding that uses labnah or strained yogurt to make a thicker fool than ordinary thick yogurt would make. The blackcurrants are left whole to retain the fibre which is in their skins. If not using meringues, you might want to increase the quantity of sugar to 75g (3oz). **Serves 4**

50g (2oz) unrefined caster sugar
4 tablespoons elderflower cordial or crème de cassis
400g (14oz) blackcurrants (the ready-prepared frozen ones are easiest to use)
265g (9½oz) labnah or strained yogurt (see page 74)
2 large meringue nests or 4 small meringues, or Almond and Polenta Biscuits (see page 137), to serve

Dissolve the sugar in the elderflower cordial or crème de cassis in a saucepan over a gentle heat.

Mix the sugar liquid with the blackcurrants and purée well in a food processor. Allow to cool, then add the labnah or strained yogurt. Mix briefly and taste to check for the right balance of sweetness and sharpness.

If using meringues, break up into bite-sized pieces and place in the bottom of four pretty glasses or ramekins or small bowls. Spoon over the blackcurrant fool and serve straight away or no more than 1 hour later – don't prepare too far in advance or the meringue will become too soft and gooey.

If serving with biscuits, place the fool in glasses or bowls, cover with clingfilm and leave in the fridge to firm up for several hours beforehand.

Fibre rating: MEDIUM
Per serving with meringue: 3.6g fibre, 145 kcals, 1g fat, 0g saturated fat, 0.05g sodium

Date-filled sticky toffee pudding

This might not be the healthiest of puddings, but at least it is high in fibre! The darker the sugar, the darker-looking the sponge. I find that yogurt works very well with this pudding as it balances the sweetness of the sauce. **Serves 6**

175g (6oz) stoned dates, finely chopped

150g (5oz) unsalted butter, softened

150g (5oz) dark soft brown sugar

2 medium eggs

125g (4½oz) wholemeal flour

50g (2oz) bran

1 teaspoon baking powder

For the sauce

100g (3½oz) dark soft brown sugar

75g (3oz) unsalted butter

3 tablespoons double cream

Low-fat bio yogurt or double cream, to serve (optional)

First make the sauce by placing all the ingredients in a saucepan and melting slowly over a very low heat until the sugar has dissolved, then simmer gently for 1 minute. Pour the mixture into the base of a 500g (18oz) loaf tin or individual ramekins or dariole moulds. Set aside to cool.

Preheat the oven to 180°C/350°F/gas mark 4.

Place the dates in a saucepan with 200ml (7fl oz) water and bring to the boil. Simmer for about 5 minutes until the dates have softened and the liquid completely evaporated. Set aside to cool.

Cream the butter and sugar until it becomes paler in colour and then add the eggs one at a time, beating well. Add the flour, bran, baking powder and cooled dates and gently fold in. Spoon this mixture on top of the sauce in the tin(s) and bake in the oven for about 20–40 minutes, depending on the size of the tin(s). Check every 10–15 minutes: when firm to the touch and a knife comes out clean when carefully placed into the centre, the sponge is cooked.

Turn the tin(s) upside down to unmould the sponge and serve with either yogurt or cream, if you like.

Fibre rating: HIGH

Per serving not including yogurt or cream to serve: 5.4g fibre, 648 kcals, 42g fat, 26g saturated fat, 0.13g sodium

Wholemeal plum crumble *A simple*

crumble with added goodies to make it healthy. Substitute apricots for the plums if you wish; use fruit that is in season and that suits your fibre needs. For a lower fibre option you could use white flour instead of wholemeal flour. **Serves 4**

450g (1lb) ripe plums

25g (1oz) unrefined caster sugar (optional)

Low-fat bio yogurt or vanilla ice cream, to serve (optional)

For the crumble topping

125g (4½oz) wholemeal flour

1 heaped tablespoon bran

50g (2oz) rolled oats

25g (1oz) sesame seeds

50g (2oz) unrefined caster sugar

½ teaspoon ground cinnamon or ginger

60g (2½oz) sunflower margarine, cut into small pieces

60g (2½oz) butter, cut into small pieces

Preheat the oven to 180°C/350°F/gas mark 4.

Cut the plums in half and remove the stones. Place the plums in a 23 x 18cm (9 x 7in) gratin dish and sprinkle over the sugar, if using.

To make the topping, place the dry ingredients in a bowl and, using the tips of your fingers, rub in the margarine and butter to create a coarse meal consistency. Scatter over the plums and bake in the oven for about 30 minutes, until the fruit is soft and the crumble golden brown.

Serve with a dollop of yogurt, or vanilla ice cream if you are allowed.

Fibre rating: HIGH

Per serving: 6.4g fibre, 475 kcals, 30g fat, 14g saturated fat, 0.18g sodium

Fig and cranberry bistaya cake

This 'cake' is inspired by one from Morocco, where a pastry similar to filo is filled with savoury as well as sweet fillings. The ingredients make it quite Christmassy, but it can be enjoyed at any time of year. Use fresh pears or apples instead of figs if you prefer. **Serves 6**

50g (2oz) whole almonds or
    pistachio nuts
75g (3oz) dried cranberries
350g (12oz) dried figs, diced
25g (1oz) brown sugar
1 teaspoon ground cinnamon
1 piece chopped stem ginger
1 tablespoon syrup from the
    stem ginger

2 tablespoons lemon, orange
    or apple juice
125g (4½oz) filo pastry (about
    10 small sheets or 6 large
    sheets)
25ml (1fl oz) sunflower oil
Icing sugar, to decorate

Preheat the oven to 150°C/300°F/gas mark 3. Roast the nuts for about 10 minutes, until golden brown, then chop coarsely. Turn the oven up to 180°C/350°F/gas mark 4, ready to bake the pastry.

Place the nuts, cranberries, figs, sugar, cinnamon, ginger and lemon, orange or apple juice in a bowl and mix well. Set aside to infuse for at least 10 minutes.

Line a baking tray with baking parchment. Place 1 large or 2 slightly overlapping smaller sheets of filo pastry on the tray and brush with sunflower oil. Cover with 3 or 6 more sheets of filo, brushing each layer with oil.

Place the fruit mixture in the middle, spreading it out to form a circle about 20cm (8in) diameter and leaving a good margin of pastry around the outside. Fold up the pastry like a circular envelope. Brush with oil and place 2 sheets of filo on top, oiling each layer and trimming the pastry as necessary if using large sheets. Tuck a little of the filo underneath the 'cake' to create a neat top. Finally brush with oil and bake in the oven for about 30 minutes, until the pastry is a light golden brown.

Leave to cool and dust with icing sugar before serving.

Fibre rating: HIGH
Per serving: 5.7g fibre, 348 kcals, 16g fat, 3g saturated fat, 0.1g sodium

Index

alcohol 33
almond and polenta biscuits 137
aloe vera 35
apricots 99
    apricot muffins 52–53
asparagus and potato frittata 74
asparagus and red onion tart 108–109
asparagus, bacon and chickpea salad 70–71
asparagus stir-fried with sesame seeds 108
aubergines with miso 116
avocado, fennel and cucumber relish 81

bacon 70–71, 131
barley 58, 119
beans 67, 78, 94, 104, 130
    borlotti bean salad with broccoli, pinenuts
        and anchovies 127
    chicken broth with broccoli and cannellini
        beans 63
    red rice with green beans and beetroot
        126–127
    stir-fried tofu with peppers and black bean
        sauce 110–111
    swordfish with cannellini beans 92
beef and butter bean stew with peppers 104
beef and potato hash 48
beef brisket pot-roast 100
beetroot 126–127
    chilled beetroot and dill soup 62
biscuits 39, 137
blackcurrant fool 138–139
bread 55, 68–69, 81, 105
    bruschetta with chard, borlotti beans and
        anchovy sauce 78
    focaccia 48–49
    wholemeal soda bread 52
broccoli 63, 94, 111, 127
butternut squash and onions with feta 120–121

cabbage 102–103
    braised red cabbage with raisins and
        orange 118
caffeine 33
caramelised pears with walnuts and raisins 138
carrot, ginger and radicchio salad 67
carrots with braised fennel 117
celeriac remoulade 71

celeriac, tomatoes and olives 121
cereals 38
chard 78
cheese 113, 130–131
chicken
    chicken and prune stew 104
    chicken broth with broccoli and cannellini
        beans 63
    grilled chicken sandwich 105
    noodle broth with chicken 58–59
    Persian chicken with rice 100
chickpea, bacon and asparagus salad 70–71
chickpea flat bread 55
chickpea salad with Thai-style squid 128
chickpea stew with aubergines, courgettes
    and tomatoes 129
chickpeas with meatballs 101
chocolate fridge cake 136–137
courgettes 98, 113, 129
    courgette and cumin salad 65
couscous 93
crackers 39
cranberry and fig bistaya cake 141
cucumber, avocado, and fennel relish 81
cumin and courgette salad 65

date-filled sticky toffee pudding 140
diet 18–21, 44–45
    assessing 16–17
    fibre 22–25, 31, 41
    fluid 32–33
    sample menus 42–43
drinks 32–33
duck breast salad with endive and oranges 64
duck breasts with garam masala 98

eating out 39–40
eggs Florentine 50–51
endives 64
    baked endive wrapped in prosciutto 76

fennel 61, 66, 81
    fennel braised with carrots 117
fibre 22–25, 31, 41
fig and cranberry bistaya cake 141
fig and walnut rye bread 55
fish
    anchovies 78, 127
    baked fish parcels with julienne of
        vegetables 88–89
    kedgeree 51

mackerel simmered in miso soup 88
monkfish kebabs marinated with herbs
    and yogurt 86
salmon with lentils and spinach 92
salmon wrapped in vine leaves with
    couscous 93
swordfish with cannellini beans 92
Syrian stuffed fish with rice and tamarind 87
tuna Niçoise with a pulse 94
focaccia with potatoes, cherry tomatoes
    and rosemary 48–49
food intolerance 31
food shopping 37–39
fruit 39, 137
    fruit compote 54

ginger, carrot and radicchio salad 67
grains 38, 52, 130
grappa and peach sorbet 134
greens 112

herbs 48–49, 62, 63, 86, 130
houmous 105

IBS 7, 8, 41, 44–45
    symptoms 10–13, 26–29
    treatment 14–15

lactose intolerance 34
lamb wrapped in cabbage leaves 102–103
leek and yellow pepper bake 113
lemon grass fish broth 90–91
lentils 66, 92
    lentil salad with bacon and grilled
        peppers 131

meatballs with chickpeas 101
menus 42–43
miso 88, 116
muesli 54
mushrooms 98, 99, 112, 129
    wild mushroom and bread salad 66
    wild mushroom and tomato soup 60–61

noodle broth with chicken 58–59
noodles with tofu and vegetables 112
nutrition see diet
nuts 39, 68, 84, 127, 130, 137
    caramelised pears with walnuts and raisins 138
    dukkah (Egyptian nut dip) 78
    rye bread with figs and walnuts 55

olives 94, 113, 121
onions 67, 68
    asparagus and red onion tart 108–109
    roast butternut squash and onions with
        feta 120–121
oranges 64, 118

pasta 38–39
    buckwheat pasta with spinach, mushrooms
        and truffle oil 129
    faro pasta salad with tomatoes, cannellini
        beans and basil 130
    minestrone with pearl barley 58
    pasta with clams 124–125
pea and potato pasties 114–115
pea and tarragon soup 63
peach and grappa sorbet 134
pears with walnuts and raisins 138
peppermint 34
peppers 104, 105
    grilled peppers with raisins, red onions
        and pinenuts 68
    leek and yellow pepper bake 113
    lentil salad with bacon and grilled
        peppers 131
    stir-fried tofu with peppers and black
        bean sauce 110–111
plum crumble 140
polenta grilled with prawns 95
potatoes
    asparagus and potato frittata 74
    beef and potato hash 48
    focaccia with potatoes, cherry tomatoes
        and rosemary 48–49
    mashed tatties in their skins 118
    mini pea and potato pasties 114–115
    potato galette with wholemeal
        pastry 80–81
    potato-base pizza with courgettes, olives
        and ricotta 113
    warm potato salad with green beans, spring
        onions and chives 67
probiotics and prebiotics 34–35
prosciutto 76
pulses 38, 94
pumpkin and broccoli with tofu
    curry 111
pumpkin risotto 124

quail stuffed with apricots and wild
    mushrooms 99

radicchio, carrot and ginger salad 67
raisins 68, 118, 128, 138
rice 38–39, 87, 100
    kedgeree 51
    pumpkin risotto 124
    red rice with green beans and beetroot
        126–127
    saffron and raisin rice 128
    wild rice and spelt with chestnuts
        and sesame seeds 130
rye bread with figs and walnuts 55

sardine kofta with tomatoes and spices 84
seeds 39, 52, 108, 130
sesame 108, 117, 119, 130
shellfish
    grilled polenta with prawns, Venetian style
        95
    mussel, saffron and yogurt stew 85
    pasta with clams 124–125
    scallop salad with olives, broccoli and beans
        94
    shrimps on toast 79
    Thai prawn balls in lemon grass fish broth
        90–91
    Thai squid and chickpea salad 128
sorbitol 34
spices 61, 84, 85, 98, 128
spinach 92, 129
spinach, fennel and lentil salad 66
spinach with sesame sauce Japanese style 119
strawberry cheesecake 134–135
symbiotics 34–35

tabbouleh 65
tamarind 62, 87
toffee pudding 140
tofu
    Oriental steamed tofu with mushrooms
        and greens 112
    stir-fried tofu with peppers and black bean
        sauce 110–111
    tofu curry with pumpkin and broccoli 111
    tofu-sesame dipping sauce with steamed
        vegetables 117
tomatoes 48–49, 129, 130
    roasted celeriac, tomatoes and olives 121
    sardine kofta with tomatoes and spices 84
    tomato and tamarind soup 62
    wild mushroom and tomato soup 60–61
trout with almonds 84

vegetables 88–89, 112, 117
    roasted winter vegetables with pearl
        barley 119
    wholemeal pitta bread and vegetable salad
        68–69
vegetarianism 35
venison stir-fry with courgettes and
    mushrooms 98
vine leaves 93
    stuffed vine leaves 77

watercress and fennel soup with Indian
    spices 61
weight gain 31

yogurt 86
    marinated labnah balls 74–75
    mussel, saffron and yogurt stew 85

Resources

UK

The IBS Research Appeal
PO Box 18
Crowborough
East Sussex TN6 1ZY
www.ibsresearchupdate.org.uk
www.please-help-my-ibs.org

IBS Network
Northern General Hospital
Sheffield S5 7AU
Helpline: 01543 492 192 (Mon–Fri 6–8pm,
Sat 10–12am)
info@ibsnetwork.org.uk
www.ibsnetwork.org.uk

Core
3 St Andrew's Place
London NW1 4LB
info@corecharity.org.uk
www.corecharity.org.uk

US

**International Foundation for Functional
Gastrointestinal Disorders (IFFGD)**
PO Box 170864
Milwaukee, WI 53217-8076
Tel: 414 964 1799
iffgd@iffgd.org
www.iffgd.org

IBS Self Help Group (IBSGroup)
1440 Whalley Avenue, #145
New Haven, CT 06515
ibs@ibsgroup.org
www.ibsgroup.org

IBS Association (IBSA)
Address as IBSGroup (see above)
ibsa@ibsassociation.org
www.ibsassociation.org

CANADA

IBS Self Help Group (IBSGroup)
P.O. Box 94074
Toronto, Ontario M4N 3R1
ibs@ibsgroup.org
www.ibsgroup.org

IBS Association (IBSA)
Address as IBSGroup (see above)
ibsa@ibsassociation.org
www.ibsassociation.org

**The Canadian Society of
Intestinal Research**
855 West 12th Avenue
Vancouver, British Columbia
V5Z 1M9
Tel: 604 875 4875
Toll-Free (in Canada): 1 866 600 4875
www.badgut.com

AUSTRALIA

IBIS Australia
PO Box 7092
Sippy Downs
Qld 7092
Tel: 1300 651 131
contact@ibis-australia.org
www.ibis-australia.org

First published in Great Britain 2005 by
Kyle Cathie Limited
122 Arlington Road
London NW1 7HP
general.enquiries@kyle-cathie.com
www.kylecathie.com

10 9 8 7 6 5

ISBN 978 1 85626 567 6

Sophie Braimbridge and Erica Jankovich are
hereby identified as the authors of this work
in accordance with Section 77 of the
Copyright, Designs and Patents Act 1988.

Text © 2005 Sophie Braimbridge
and Erica Jankovich
Photography © 2005 Tara Fisher
Book design © 2005 Kyle Cathie Limited

Senior Editor Muna Reyal
Editor Jennifer Wheatley
Designer Carl Hodson
Photographer Tara Fisher
Home economist Annie Rigg
Styling Penny Markham
Copy editor Ruth Baldwin
Recipe analysis Erica Jankovich
Production Sha Huxtable and Alice Holloway

A Cataloguing In Publication record for this
title is available from the British Library.

Colour reproduction by Colourscan
Printed and bound in Singapore by
Star Standard